2-vi-91.
Cambridge.

11/

C000070403

HOW TO GET WORK DONE ON YOUR HOME

HOW TO GET WORK DONE ON YOUR HOME

Robert Buchanan

KOGAN
PAGE

The table on page 64 is reproduced by permission of the
copyright holders, RIBA Publications Limited.

First published in Great Britain in 1990 by
Kogan Page Limited, 120 Pentonville Road,
London N1 9JN.

British Library Cataloguing in Publication Data
A CIP catalogue record for this book is
available from the British Library.

ISBN 1-85091-974-7

Typeset by DP Photosetting, Aylesbury, Bucks
Printed and bound in Great Britain by
Richard Clay Ltd (The Chaucer Press), Bungay

Contents

Author's Note

The term 'professional' is used throughout and can apply to an architect, surveyor, consultant, engineer or other qualified person.

The pronouns 'he', 'him' and 'his' are intended throughout to apply to both men and women and have been used for the sake of simplicity.

'Contractor' means anyone who 'contracts' or 'agrees' to carry out work in return for payment.

The legal information given in this book is not a substitute for professional legal advice, which should always be taken before starting any legal proceedings, bearing in mind that each case has its individual problems.

Chapter 1

Introduction

It has been estimated that in Britain today there are more than 21 million dwellings* constructed for residential use. Every one of these has to be maintained and at some time will need repair or improvement – from simple routine upkeep such as replacing worn-out tap washers and broken or missing roof slates to larger jobs like complete rewiring or a new kitchen.

Loft conversions (turning a loft or attic into a habitable area) and rear extensions are popular ways of improving and extending the home, and are major building operations as far as the average householder is concerned. They are often undertaken as an alternative to moving to a larger house and can be more cost-effective. (The cost of the move alone could pay for a significant amount of work on the existing home.) The benefits gained by such improvements, both in additional living space and increased market value of the property, are undeniable, although living through the actual building work can be difficult for many people.

Owning a brand new house or flat doesn't exclude you from the round of regular maintenance, although you shouldn't be liable for major repairs for a long time, providing of course that the construction or conversion work was properly carried out. Simple maintenance, whatever the property, is the most effective way to avoid many of the problems which lead to costly repairs.

Some maintenance can be carried out by householders themselves, but because of the complexity of buildings and their related services and installations, everyone sooner or later has to call in a skilled specialist of some sort.

---

* *Sources:* Office of Population Censuses and Surveys (England and Wales); General Register Office (Scotland); General Register Office (Northern Ireland).

Scope of the book

This book is intended for anyone who is ever likely to need to use builders or contractors of any kind for work on their home or small office. It covers the employment of anyone from a part-time gardener to a building contractor undertaking major works such as an extension, loft conversion or even the construction of a new house.

You probably feel, as a householder, that you can cope with getting someone in to do the small jobs like repairing the garden fence or having a couple of extra power points put in, but you may become uneasy as soon as the word 'builder' is mentioned. Often the preconceptions are based on other people's horror stories and a fear of the unknown, and on the fact that you will be opening your house to a crowd of people intent on making a lot of mess and damaging your personal property. It can happen, but building work by its very nature cannot be done without some mess, and damage, if it does occur, is rarely intentional. Maybe you have used builders before and had a nasty experience that you don't want to repeat. Being prepared for situations that arise is half the battle, and knowing how to handle them without losing your balance can help to sort out problems that occur whenever people are employed to work in your home.

Current state of the industry

The current shortage of skilled trades people in Britain exists because of a variety of factors (too numerous to go into here) which have contributed to the problem over the years.

The effects of this situation have been twofold:

- There has been an enormous rise over the past few years in do-it-yourself, or DIY, and stores now abound throughout the country, as do books and manuals, on almost all aspects of home improvement, repair and maintenance. Whether or not this works to the advantage of the homeowner depends on the suitability of the person carrying out the work. (See Chapter 3 on DIY).
- The other effect has been the rise in the number of unskilled or semi-skilled people professing to be competent at just about everything. Anybody can set up as a builder or tradesman

without qualifications or legal restriction (except in some cases, mainly where safety is an important factor). The average householder is at a disadvantage, knowing very little about building skills and being unable to afford an architect or overseer for the small jobs on his home; he has to accept a contractor at face value, as credentials and certificates are not usually available. There are properly skilled and trained contractors around, of course, but finding them is not always easy.

At the bottom of the pile are the 'cowboys' – so called because they come into town looking for work, and being unskilled, will take on anything. When the job is done they leave with your money, never to be seen again.

The most sought-after section of the workforce are those who do what is required of them to a reasonable standard and a fair price. They fit the requirements of most householders, being neither a large organisation that will cost the earth, nor a shoestring set-up, but competent, skilled individuals or small companies with access to specialist trades.

Such is the demand for people to carry out jobs in the home that the householder sometimes has little choice in whom to employ and has to take pot luck. Skilled contractors have their own standards as well, and often won't take on 'patch-up' jobs, understandably so. So such jobs are left to whoever *will* take them on. There is always the temptation for the householder to paper over the cracks this year and do a proper job next year. This is often money down the drain and in many cases what is really being put off is having a large amount of building work done, not spending the money. Many people need to be 'prepared', mentally as well as financially, for the daunting prospect of 'having the builders in', or having any sizeable amount of work done on the home, and one of the aims of this book is to help with that preparation.

The once male-dominated industry is now attracting more women. Popular trades are painting/decorating, electrical work, gardening/landscaping and even general building.

Chapter 2

Where to Start

The first thing to do when contemplating any job is to define the work that you want done and identify the person or persons who will do it.

Type of work frequently needed

Taking small jobs first, some common ones have been listed below. They relate to work on the fabric of the building and to the fixtures, installations and appliances within it. Their respective contractors are included, although many could be managed by a competent handyman. If you go to a builder who then provides a specialist it will generally cost you more than if you contact the specialist directly, as the builder will take a profit. Specialists normally advertise under the description of their service.

Small jobs

- roof repairs — roofer
- windows/doors repairs and replacements — joiner or carpenter
- decoration internal/external — painter/decorator
- blocked drains — plumber or specialist
- brickwork repointing — bricklayer or builder
- glass replacement — glazier
- plastering and sand/cement render — plasterer
- damp treatment (small areas) — specialist or builder
- ceiling repairs and replacements — plasterer or builder
- dry rot/wet rot treatment — specialist or builder
- loft insulation — builder or DIY
- blocked gutters/rainwater pipes — plumber
- built-in cupboards and wardrobes — carpenter
- all electrical jobs — electrician
- central heating repair and maintenance — heating specialist or service agent

- electrical and gas appliance repairs   – manufacturer or
  and replacements   service agent
- floor and wall tiling   – tiler
- new cold water tank   – plumber

Some of the respective tradespeople sound obvious, but using a specialist instead of a general builder should mean that you get a better job, and safety is an important factor in some of the work. Repairs, which account for many of the small jobs carried out in and around the home, are hardly ever as good as replacement, especially where roofs, windows and patching up old plasterwork are concerned. Don't expect a top class guaranteed job on items like this because you won't get it. A repair is merely the means of prolonging the life of something. However, we all have to weigh up the available cash when the choice of repair or replacement presents itself, and decide accordingly. Nevertheless, it always pays to ask the cost of replacement, whatever the job, rather than automatically assume that a repair will be vastly cheaper and will therefore do for the time being. For example, the *time* spent on the replacement of some items can be a lot less than the time spent on repair, and you should get a better, guaranteed job. Even period features such as unusual windows and plaster cornices can be made in the original style, using similar materials.

Maintenance, particularly of bathrooms, plumbing systems and central heating installations will help to avoid problems such as breakdowns and water related damage, but don't attempt makeshift repairs yourself with any water, gas or electrical installations – it isn't worth it. Apart from the safety aspect, patched up water leaks will eventually start again and the damage could run into thousands of pounds. It is also important to make sure that pipework insulation is kept intact as it can rot, or even be picked off by mice and birds.

Here is a true story:

A family went away for the Christmas period leaving the central heating system turned off. During a cold snap an unlagged cold water tank in the loft froze and burst. The temperature subsequently rose and the tank thawed and gushed its contents across the loft. The water ran down almost every wall in the house and, still being fed from the main, soaked off the wallpaper as it went. Curtains, carpets, furniture, doors were ruined as the water continued downwards. After a week the neighbours noticed water coming through the outside wall at ground level and arranged to have it turned off. Needless to say – the damage was colossal, and all for the sake of a £15 insulating jacket.

Larger jobs

- loft conversion   – specialist firm or builder
- extension to property   – builder
- underpinning   – specialist firm or builder
- electrical rewiring   – electrician
- double glazing   – specialist firm
- central heating installation   – heating specialist
- complete damp proof course   – specialist firm
- complete refurbishment   – builder and specialist trades

When contemplating major jobs on your property it is always advisable to contact an architect or surveyor for advice. You may need to use them anyway if drawings and professional management are required. You should also contact your local council in case planning approval and/or compliance with building regulations is required. (More about this in Chapter 9.)

Finding people to do the work

Finding people to take on small jobs is hardly ever easy, and when you do find them their charges are nearly always higher than you think would be warranted for minor, trivial jobs. One of the reasons is that many skilled craftsmen and tradesmen don't want jobs that require them to move tools and equipment around every day or so. The bigger jobs are far more lucrative and use their skills more effectively, so if they do take on small jobs they will price them so that they *are* worth doing. Likewise, a medium-size building firm will only really be interested in the size of job that its workforce is geared to. However, many small builders claim to tackle any job – big or small – and certainly if you have several small jobs that can all be done at the same time it will be easier to get someone to quote for them, and it will be cheaper than getting each job done separately.

The handyman and one-man concern are the people most likely to answer your request for an estimate. They won't be highly skilled at everything – nobody can be – but if they have a good working knowledge of building skills you should get a reasonable job.

So where do you go to find someone to do your job? For small jobs the most likely sources are:

- **advertisements** in local papers – many of them list a wide range of services;
- **Yellow Pages** – they cover the whole country area by area and list most types of service. There is plenty of selection but choice can sometimes be difficult;
- **shop windows** – good for small local services;
- **manufacturers** – of equipment, appliances, fixtures etc. They can have their own installers/service department or a list of approved contractors;
- **friends and neighbours** – 'word of mouth' recommendations are usually the best way of finding the right person for the job. A lot of business is conducted by this method and many contractors rely on it as a means of obtaining work and hardly ever need to advertise formally.

For medium to large jobs the most likely sources are:

- **recommendations** – again usually the best way no matter how big the job is;
- **trade organisations** – they have approved contractors (see pages 131–136);
- **Yellow Pages** – again plenty of selection but, as the contractors will probably not be known to you, great care will be needed when deciding.

Building societies can also sometimes recommend contractors but whoever you get to do your job, large or small, try to get some references as to quality of work, reliability, length of time in business, and even look at some of their other work if you think it will help.

If you are planning major alterations or perhaps an extension or loft conversion you would be advised to contact an architect or a building surveyor. He will have access to contractors, general builders and specialists, and his contact means that you can be relieved of the problem of finding them yourself. He can also run the job for you. (See Chapter 4 on professional advice.)

Contractors you should avoid using

- Unsolicited callers at your property
- Those not willing to offer any references or company details
- Those who want money in advance of actually starting the job without good reason or safeguards
- Firms that are too small, or too large, for your job.

Approaching companies and small businesses

Before you approach anybody to provide estimates or quotations, you must first decide exactly what it is that you want done. If you dither, and confuse people who come to discuss the work you are proposing by being vague and unsure, they will probably become irritated and disinterested in your job, and are likely to think that you will behave in the same way if they actually do the job. So write down what needs doing, and if there are a lot of small jobs list each one and make some reference to the quality required – for example, a cheap temporary job or top quality work.

With fairly straightforward estimating jobs (for example, the electrical rewiring of a house or flat) think beforehand about where you want power and lighting points etc. Leaving it all until the estimator is there means that a long time will be spent thinking about basic details, and the time spent on preparing estimates needs to be limited as far as the contractor is concerned, especially as they are not normally charged for.

This doesn't mean, of course, that you can't ask advice based on his experience. You would be foolish not to. But giving it some thought beforehand will help enormously, as you will have been able to assess exactly what your requirements are without the pressure of having to make quick decisions.

If you aren't specific about what you want you will probably not be happy with the estimate and will have to go back to the contractor to alter it.

Some jobs will naturally be beyond your grasp technically and it will be difficult to involve yourself in them at all. Underpinning, for example, to rectify subsidence, requires expert knowledge and handling, and you would have to confine yourself to researching which companies to ask for estimates.

If the job to be estimated is fairly large, perhaps a loft conversion, before approaching a builder for an estimate it would be advisable (as already suggested) to ask an architect about the viability of the intended work, and get him to produce drawings of the layout you require and a specification of the materials to be used. The builder can then produce an estimate based on 'drawings and specification' which will be straightforward for him as they are presented in 'trade' language, and satisfactory for you as you will have a professional base for your estimate.

Preferable as this method is, many builders are quite capable of doing not only the estimate, but also the whole job without detailed drawings, but for your peace of mind the architect method is the best, and the cost of his services will be worth it.

Another advantage of having drawings and a specification is that you can approach as many contractors as you like and know that their estimates will all be based on the same set of instructions; then the comparison of costs will be made easier.

What to ask

For any medium to large job you should always get at least three estimates and cover the following points:

- Always ask for written, not verbal, estimates.
- Ask when they could start and how long the job would take.
- Ask how any additional work would be priced.
- Ask about continuity of work.
- Ask when payment(s) would be required.
- Ask about insurance (see Chapter 8).
- If no specification is available, identify which materials you would like to be used for certain items, eg hardwood (not softwood) windows, slate (not tile) roof.
- Ask about means of access – for example, if the roof is being renewed it will be better for you that access is from the outside, otherwise everything and everyone will have to go right through the house, with the resulting mess and inconvenience.
- Ask about guarantees.
- Check that the estimate will include everything (equipment hire, materials, VAT etc).

Most of the questions apply to whatever type of job is being estimated, and when you are discussing the details make sure that you both understand each other. If there is something you are not certain about, go over it again; if a technical word or jargon is used, ask for an explanation.

The builder or contractor may also need to know, especially with large contracts, how you will be funding the job. Will you, for example, have to raise a bank loan or increase your mortgage? He may ask because loans for home improvements are sometimes held back until a certain percentage of the work has been completed, and in such a case you will have to provide some payment from other sources so the job can be started. Obviously, a loan would have to be agreed in writing before work was started. The contractor may ask about money at this stage because a complicated job could take several days to produce an estimate for, and he won't want to waste his time. If you use an architect or other professional to design *and* manage your job, he could arrange contractors and would act as intermediary between you and them, but naturally the cost of the job would increase to cover his fees. Where larger jobs are concerned, the best results generally come from those which have been designed and managed by a good professional.

To sum up:

- Decide exactly what you want – and make notes.
- For large jobs have drawings and specifications prepared.
- When contacting companies be direct and to the point. Make appointments for specific times, not 'sometime in the afternoon' and if they don't keep appointments without contacting you – forget them.
- When contacting individuals again be direct and to the point, but bear in mind that the man who does the estimating is the same man who will do the job, so if he says he will call on his way home between six and eight o'clock, that should be acceptable. As a single operator he will never be quite sure how long his day's work will take and will tend to finish the job he is doing before leaving for the night, and as salesman, workforce, office staff, director and teaboy he is a busy man, so a little leeway in your dealings with him is sometimes called for.
- Get estimates in writing.
- Some jobs are so small that a written estimate would be silly – for example, a new tap washer.

- Decide on the quality (and therefore the price) of workmanship and materials you require and approach contractors accordingly.
- Some individuals and small concerns are not registered for VAT (legally) so if you use them you won't have to pay VAT on the labour content of the job. (VAT is levied on all materials at source – so everyone pays it.)

Chapter 3
Do It Yourself

It is not intended to cover 'do-it-yourself' in any great depth. This chapter may serve as a guide to those who are having work done in their homes by contractors and who would like to carry out some of the work themselves, either to save money or just because they want to put some of their own handiwork into their properties. Quite often the finishing jobs (painting, decorating, tiling etc) are the best for the DIY enthusiast to take on because they are time-consuming for the contractor and therefore expensive for the client. Also, as the contractor can leave the site when his part of the work is done, you won't get in each other's way. Those more competent at DIY may wish to take on some of the larger jobs while using contractors for specialist work. Again, try to separate the jobs so that you don't get in each other's way.

DIY is unbeatable for very small jobs, but when tackling larger jobs one cautionary maxim still applies – the amount of experience gained equals the amount of equipment ruined. So a realistic assessment of your abilities should always be made.

Difficulties in (a) finding and (b) being able to afford people to work on houses and other properties have been major contributing factors in the rise of the do-it-yourself (or DIY) industry. DIY superstores are now to be found all over Britain, and manuals explaining how to do just about everything from changing a fuse to building a house are readily available.

Some people, no matter how hard they try, just do not have the ability or the knack to carry out practical tasks, and are unable to convert instructions in a book into practical reality. However, those with some practical knowledge and understanding can, with a reasonable tool kit, step-by-step instructions and the necessary time (one of the hardest things to find) carry out quite major work at home. It goes without saying that you won't get a professional job without practical experience, but you will have the satisfaction of doing it and, most important, in the *way you* want it done.

Attention to detail is what makes any job look well done. For example, the all-time favourite – putting up bookshelves – can be made to look something special if everything is straight and level, the shelves are edged with hardwood strip, and the completed job is sanded smooth. Some examples of popular DIY jobs are:

Simple jobs

- Painting and decorating
- Tiling
- Loft insulation
- Minor electrical/plumbing jobs
- Shelves.

Larger jobs

- Fitted kitchen
- Built-in wardrobes
- Central heating
- New bathroom
- Bricklaying.

These are examples of the type of job well within the grasp of someone with a good basic practical knowledge and the perseverance to see them through. Practical guides about how to do the above jobs are available from bookshops and public libraries.

Safety

Before you tackle any job in the home you must consider the safety aspect. You can injure yourself quite badly just falling off a chair, especially if there are building materials lying around, so for a start always keep work areas free from obstruction.

You should also make sure that both you and the house are properly insured. If the work you intend doing could affect a neighbour's property, insurance should cover him too. Inform your neighbours if the work you are doing could affect them. For example, if you have to turn off their water for a whole weekend while you fit a garden tap, talk to them first!

Before doing any work connected with water systems make sure that you know where all the relevant stopcocks are *and* that they work.

When working on electrical systems make sure that you understand them and that they are properly tested when the job is complete. If you are unsure about anything that you have done in the house, get a qualified person to check it for you – it's worth it.

If you hire tools, equipment and plant from a hire shop you will probably be asked to sign a hire agreement form saying that you understand how to use them and that you accept responsibility for their use. For example, some power tools should only be used with protective equipment such as goggles and gloves, and if you fail to use them claims against the hirer in the event of an accident could prove difficult.

Pitfalls

The common pitfalls for the DIY enthusiast are:

- damage to property
- personal injury
- flood
- taking on jobs that are too large/too complicated
- getting fed up halfway through the job and abandoning it
- paying too much for materials and equipment
- underestimating the cost/extent of the job.

You can try to avoid the pitfalls by careful assessment before you start. Always leave a contingency sum available for extras and errors and be realistic when estimating the time that you have available. (You know your own limits.) Always put safety first.

Cost savings in relation to time available

If you are taking on a job in order to save money, ie not paying a contractor, bear in mind that the contractor will probably do in a day or two what will take you a week. If time is not important to you then it doesn't matter, but taking a week off work without pay will be false economy – it will be better to keep your income and pay the contractor.

Chapter 4

Help, Advice and the Professionals

Whether or not you intend organising your job yourself or employing a professional to do it for you, you will need some initial help and advice.

Smallish jobs (see page 12) would not normally need the services of a professional, but this doesn't prevent you from asking their advice. The consultation fee could save you a lot of time and trouble in locating contractors and handling the job, and the larger the job the more useful this advice would be.

A large job tends to be complicated and can involve several different contractors with different skills. You would have to decide whether you were able to organise and run a job like this or whether you should employ a professional to do part or all of it for you. You might say to yourself 'Do I need an architect to give me advice?'. The best way to find out is to chat to other people about the jobs they have had done and how they managed; contact your Citizens' Advice Bureau; ask an architect himself.

This chapter is concerned with getting advice and help from a variety of sources, and describes also the sort of professional who is used to dealing with domestic contracts.

Information and free advice

Banks will advise on the best way of funding your work and on some legal matters.

Building societies will also advise on ways of funding work. Most produce leaflets for people wanting to improve their homes. If you already have a mortgage, you should inform them anyway if you are planning work which may increase the value of your home, as it may affect insurance cover.

Builders. Many are very helpful and will, as well as giving you an estimate, advise on a variety of building products and their suitability for your home, cost comparisons, and generally what is available. They can also offer technical information and information about local authority requirements.

Builders merchants. If you are buying from them, a good builders merchant will advise on which materials are available, cost comparisons, durability etc.

Citizens' Advice Bureaux will advise on the whole range of matters relating to having work done on the home, from simple jobs to legal matters.

Friends/neighbours. Hearing about other people's home improvements, whether good experiences or bad, can be an eye-opener. They may also know what can and can't be done to your type of property (a time-saver) and be able to recommend contractors. Their experiences will be extremely useful as far as do's and don'ts are concerned.

Gas, electricity and water authorities will advise (and inspect) on safety requirements and by-laws. They also have lists of approved contractors.

Inland Revenue will advise on tax matters relating to employing contractors and sub-contractors.

Insurance companies/brokers will tell you what risks are involved when employing contractors, and will advise on your particular requirements.

Libraries have titles on most topics relating to work in the home, including DIY. They can also offer consumer advice.

Local councils automatically become involved when certain building word is carried out (drainage, conversions to flats etc). The relevant departments will advise on planning and building regulations, and how to go about obtaining the necessary approvals. They will also advise on grants. They have a wealth of information available relating to building work, and are almost always very helpful.

Trade organisations are listed on pages 131–136. They will recommend contractors, operate insurance schemes and arrange arbitration in cases of dispute. They are well worth contacting, especially for the larger jobs.

Professionals – who they are and what they do

There are several types of professional whose services you may need when having work done on your home. The main ones are described here.

Architects

The main professional body representing architects is the Royal Institute of British Architects (RIBA), although not all architects belong to it. Members of the RIBA are allowed to use the designatory letters RIBA, FRIBA and ARIBA after their names.

In Scotland the professional body is the Royal Incorporation of Architects in Scotland, and its members use the designatory letters ARIAS or FRIAS after their names.

No one in the United Kingdom may use the title 'architect' unless registered by the Architects Registration Council of the United Kingdom (ARCUK), and registration is only permitted for qualified architects.

Traditionally, an architect is concerned mainly with design, layout and what is possible and practicable in a given situation. He will want to inject style into his work, and by going to an architect you would be asking him not just for a practical plan of your scheme, but also his view of how it should look.

The ideas and designs he produces for you are based on his 'brief'. The brief is the basic information that you must supply the architect with in order for him to produce a design. For example, for a start you would need to write down some basic details of the work that you wanted done. You would also need to give an idea of how much money you were prepared to spend. There would be meetings with the architect to discuss your requirements and various details, and he would put forward suggestions and ideas regarding your project. Once the necessary information was assembled he would produce a design. Obviously, he would help and advise on what was suitable and what complied with current building and safety regulations.

Although many architects will handle quite minor jobs, especially those concerning the structure of a building, they will normally become involved with the larger jobs on the home. Make sure that the architect you choose is used to handling domestic contracts, in which case his knowledge will cover most aspects of home improvement and will include advice on planning requirements and any other local authority involvement. The services an architect could provide are:

- advice on your project
- design and drawings
- obtaining competitive estimates or advising on the selection of contractors
- inspection/administration of the whole project.

He can do some or all of these depending on whether you want to organise the actual work yourself, how much money you have available etc. A booklet, *Architect's Appointment (Small Works)*, is available from the RIBA (£1.20), which describes the services an architect provides, the terms of engagement and the recommended fees and expenses. A brochure is also available entitled 'Working with your Architect', which can be obtained from architects themselves.

Surveyors

The professional body representing surveyors is the Royal Institution of Chartered Surveyors (RICS). Members use the designatory letters ARICS or FRICS after their names. Not all surveyors are chartered and the general term 'surveyor' can be used by various people. The types of surveyor generally encountered when contemplating work on the home are:

- building surveyors
- quantity surveyors
- general practice surveyors.

Building surveyors have always been concerned more with the technical side of building operations, but nowadays are on a par with architects in being able to organise and run whole home improvement projects for clients. Surveyors may be more suited to some jobs than architects, especially those that are technically complex.

The services of a *quantity surveyor* are sometimes required as part of a building contract. His job is to provide a *bill of quantities*, which is a specification of the work to be priced for each trade or section of work. This has the advantage that every part of the work is itemised, and allows the contractor to work out costs accurately and arrive readily at a total figure for the job. It also allows the architect and the client to monitor carefully where the money is going and easily alter or cut out sections if savings are required. The quantity surveyor is also responsible for measuring the amount of work completed or installed at agreed stages throughout the contract, called valuations (see page 55). At the end of the job he makes a final measurement, including any additions and deletions, and prepares final accounts.

Obviously, his services cost money, and the decision about whether or not to use him on a particular contract depends on the size, complexity and standards required, and the availability of funds.

General practice surveyors will carry out structural surveys and a variety of other operations associated with building work.

Contact the RICS for advice on the selection of chartered surveyors in any part of the United Kingdom. The RICS also publishes a practice note – 'Structural Surveys of Residential Property' – which is available from their offices.

Structural engineers

Their professional body is the Institution of Structural Engineers (ISE) and their designatory letters for chartered members are CEng, MIStructE or CEng, FIStructE. As their title implies, they are concerned with the structure of buildings and are employed, often on an architect's recommendation to calculate dimensions and strengths of beams, foundations and other load-bearing parts of a building.

They will also carry out a *structural inspection* of a building which, they say, differs from a *structural survey* carried out by a surveyor. If you need a report on the structural condition of your house it would be worth contacting both the RICS (see page 130) and the ISE (see page 131) to discover which type of survey is required.

Other services

Designers
An interior designer is concerned with producing stylish and fashionable schemes for the interior of a property, relating to decor, general layout, colour schemes, matching ideas for furniture and fabrics and most other things that relate to the overall effect

and appearance of the inside of the home. The designer, like the architect, will have his own style which, with your financial limits in mind, he will want to impose in a way that allows him to use his artistic flair. He will assess your requirements and then produce his ideas of what he thinks will work.

There are also other specialist designers – kitchens, conservatories, patios – and if you want a stylistic finish to your project then they are the people to see. If you intend using both an architect and a designer on the same project, try to ensure that their respective operations don't clash.

Accountant

If you have one he will advise on tax-efficient ways to pay for home improvements and the best methods of borrowing based on your individual circumstances.

Solicitor

You probably won't need one unless there is a serious dispute between you and your contractor or professional, but his explanation of the wording of contracts would be worth having (before signing).

Finding a professional

As with builders, the best way to find a professional is by recommendation. Friends, neighbours and associates are the first people to contact, and if any of them have used a professional before the sort of questions you should ask are:

- Were the drawings and designs acceptable to the client and usable by the contractor?
- Was the job properly and regularly inspected?
- How good was the relationship with both contractor and client?
- Were there any disputes, and if so how were they resolved?
- Were there any payment problems?
- What was the cost of employing the professional?
- Was the specification for workmanship and materials acceptable?
- Did the professional arrange contractors himself?
- Was there a satisfactory conclusion to the job?

Architects and surveyors are now permitted to advertise, so newspapers and certain magazines would have a selection of companies and individuals to contact. Try to find one that lives within a reasonable distance of your home, as travelling time and expenses can be costly, and they would go on your bill. Make sure, also, that whoever you employ carries professional indemnity insurance (Chapter 8), and finally that they are experienced in handling the type of job that you want done. The RIBA and the RICS provide lists of their members who will take on work in your area. They will also advise on the suitability of their members for the type of work you require.

Chapter 5

Raising Finance

The way in which you raise money to pay for home improvements and repairs will depend in part on your personal circumstances. Even if you have cash available it might be more tax-effective to extend your mortgage (if you have one) and use any cash you may have for something else, not tax-allowable. A chat with your building society, bank manager or accountant will provide details.

If you don't have cash available then you will *have* to borrow and, as with buying anything, including money, it pays to shop around. The first steps are to see your bank manager, building society manager or financial adviser and enquire about interest rates, repayment periods and tax position.

Banks

Different schemes for loaning money are available but the basic methods are:

- secured loans
- unsecured loans
- overdrafts.

A *secured loan* is one which requires the security of any assets you may have in order to cover the amount borrowed. Assets could be anything valuable but for most homeowners a 'charge' taken on their home would be a convenient method. A charge means that the bank has an interest in your home, and that if you were to default on the loan repayments the bank could, as a last resort, force the sale of your home. They would then be entitled to repayment of the loan from the proceeds of the sale. Fortunately, this doesn't happen very often, and if people do get into financial difficulty, perhaps resulting from the loss of a job, the bank would probably agree to suspend the repayments for a while, or maybe extend the loan period. A secured loan can be made available for a substantial amount, as long as you have the assets and income to cover it, so you have to be careful when calculating the cost of repayments in relation to your earnings.

An *unsecured loan* is one taken without security, but certain conditions would have to prevail before it was granted, and it would generally be for a smaller amount.

An *overdraft* can be granted at the bank manager's discretion and would be subject to your financial position. The manager is likely to be less keen on this method of loaning money, but as far as you are concerned it allows a lot of flexibility that a straight loan doesn't. For example:

> You wish to borrow £5000 for work on your home which will take several months. With a straightforward loan over three years (say) the whole sum would be paid into your account and you would start paying interest on the total outstanding from day one. With an overdraft facility you would only pay interest when you dipped into the red, (apart from a small setting-up fee). So if the £5000 was payable to contractors in stages (perhaps £1000 per month) you would only pay interest on the amount by which you were overdrawn, and any money in the account already would stave off interest charges even longer, as would your regular salary cheques and any other payments into your account

One of the drawbacks with having an overdraft is that you may be asked to clear it at fairly short notice if it goes over the time originally agreed.

When working out your ability to make repayments for loans don't forget that interest rates can vary.

Building societies

If you already have a mortgage it is usually easy to extend it to cover the cost of work on your home. It will depend on the value of your home in relation to your existing mortgage and your financial status. It is one of the cheapest types of loan that you can get and, depending on the size of the mortgage and your personal circumstances, will entitle you to tax relief. (The current limit for tax relief is £30,000.)

If you don't already have a mortgage it might be worth considering taking one on. There are several factors to take into account – age, valuation fees, whether you would qualify for tax relief, the time required to set it up etc. Some building societies insist that you must have been a saver with them for a certain period before they will grant a mortgage, but shopping around will reveal which do and which don't. Availability of mortgages is also dependent upon the financial climate of the day. Interest rates, the number of applications and the amount of cash available all influence how much and to whom the societies will lend.

The building societies, like the banks, will generally be sympathetic and helpful if you encounter temporary financial problems. Interest rates vary from time to time, as they do with banks, and a rise or fall by one tends to be matched by the other – to some degree at least. The status of some building societies appears to be changing (flotation of the Abbey National in 1989). They seem to be aligning themselves more with the banks and some are offering straightforward loans for a variety of purposes. This is doubtless in response to the fact that some banks now offer mortgages (although with limitations).

Credit cards/plastic money

You can use your plastic card up to its limit but it is a very expensive way of borrowing money, especially over a long period. 'Master' loans operated by card companies might be easily obtainable, but compare interest rates with equivalent bank loans. Overall, this is an expensive way to borrow money.

Other loans

Be wary of companies offering fast loans with little or no security – commonly known as 'loan sharks'. They often advertise in the small-ads columns of newspapers and magazines. They arrange loans, but at extortionate interest rates and with small-print clauses designed to force you into bankruptcy if you can't keep up the payments.

Equity release schemes

Also be careful of the crop of recent schemes which allow you to capitalise on the value of your home by borrowing a percentage of its current market value. The capital sum and the interest are then added together and not repaid until you sell the house, or until you die. These schemes are designed to benefit elderly homeowners and work reasonably well as long as the rate of increase in property values is more than interest rates. But with the slowdown in house prices and the current (1989) high interest rates, those in the schemes could be forced to repay the sum borrowed sooner than intended, and that may mean having to sell the property.

If you want to use such a scheme you should contact your bank manager or an accountant for details.

Grants

Home improvement grants are awarded by local authorities, ie your local District, Borough or City Council. The types of grant are listed below but, apart from mandatory grants, they are not always available and depend on how much money the council has at its disposal. They are:

● repairs grants
● intermediate grants
● improvement grants
● common parts grants
● special grants
● insulation grants.

Repairs grants are for houses and flats built before 1919 and are for substantial and structural repairs only, not routine maintenance work like rewiring. The grants are normally discretionary, but if you have been served with a repair notice (Housing Act 1985) the council has to give you a grant. The serving of a repair notice means that the council insists that you carry out certain work to your property.

Intermediate grants cover the installation of standard amenities where these do not already exist, for example:

● bath, shower or handbasin

- hot and cold water
- inside toilet.

They are not available for properties built after 1961 (except for disabled use). The grants are based on tables published by the Department of the Environment (DOE) in Housing Booklet No 14, and each item is listed with the relevant sum of money available. Each figure represents the maximum amount that the work should cost, and the grant allocated to you would be a percentage of that figure. The balance would have to be provided by you.

Improvement grants are for major improvements and conversions to flats and are always discretionary. They are not available for houses built after 1961.

Common parts grants are for the improvement or repair of the common parts (entrance hall, stairways etc) of properties which are separated into flats. Again, they are available for properties built before 1961 only, and are discretionary.

Special grants are only available to landlords and are discretionary unless the council has served a notice which requires the work to be carried out. They relate to houses in multiple occupation where tenants share facilities and are for the provision of standard amenities.

Insulation grants are for houses built before 1976 that have no insulation in their lofts.

Detailed information on all these grants is available in Housing Booklet No 14 (published by the DOE) or from your local authority, who will also advise on current availability and waiting lists.

Conditions for obtaining grants
Grants are not available for second or holiday homes.

Grants are not available for the whole cost of the work.

If you qualify for a grant it must be awarded before any work actually starts. This means that you must approach your local authority well in advance of the intended start date of your work.

You will need estimates for the work to submit with your application. You will have to follow the authority's guidelines on how the work is done. The authorities have their own sets of rules relating to standards of materials and workmanship, and will inspect your job to make sure that everything is as it should be before handing over the money.

You may be asked to sign an undertaking that, should you move house within five years, you would agree to pay back a proportion of the grant. This safeguard is intended to stop people from making a profit from the sale of improved properties by selling and moving on once they are finished. The Home Improvements Officer at your local council office will advise about conditions relating to specific grants.

Eligibility for grants
There are three categories of people who can apply for grants. They are:

* owner occupiers (including leaseholders)
* landlords
* tenants.

Not all grants are available to all three categories, and you should contact your Home Improvements Officer for details.

Other grants
The DOE provides grants for listed buildings, ie those which have some special historical or architectural value, and which are given part or total protection in order that their features may be preserved. If you live in a listed building you may qualify for a grant, but the likelihood of being able to obtain one easily is fairly remote, and probably not worth the effort.

A free booklet, *Paying for Repairs and Improvements to your Home*, is available from the DOE.

Chapter 6

Estimates, Contracts and Drawings

This chapter describes types of estimate and contract that would be encountered when you were organising work yourself. There is also a section devoted to a type of contract that is used if a professional is employed to run your job for you.

Estimates

A good piece of business advice is 'get everything in writing'. Sound as this advice is, in practice it is not always possible or even worthwhile when trying to get small jobs done in the home. This chapter deals with the occasions when verbal estimates are acceptable, and those when written estimates are necessary.

One of the first rules about employing people is – never tell them to start work until you have an estimate. If the job is difficult to estimate for any reason, at least get some idea of cost based on the time it will take and the cost of any materials, otherwise the final bill could be a nasty shock.

Verbal estimates
For a small job, say replacing a door or decorating a small room, a verbal estimate will probably suffice as long as the details of it are understood. For example, is it a *fixed* price, and does it include labour, materials, hire of equipment and VAT (in other words – everything)? If you are at all unsure about the person you are employing or just don't understand whether everything is included, get it in writing. Very small jobs, like having a pane of glass replaced in a window, require so little time and expense that a written estimate would be pointless.

Don't accept estimates over the phone unless the contractor has seen the job first and the details have been agreed, or unless the price is fixed anyway, eg a call-out charge.

If an insurance company is paying for any work to be done,

perhaps as a result of water damage or burglary, you need written estimates.

Written estimates

One of the benefits of having written estimates, which are essential for large jobs, is that, if they carry sufficient detail, everything that is to be done is there in black and white, and you know exactly what you are getting. Also, having the estimate in front of you will allow you to appraise the work you intend having done and consider any alterations or additions.

Some estimates, although seeming to cover everything you have asked for, offer very little in the way of detail, either as a deliberate policy by the contractor to allow him to use cheap materials and sub-standard labour, or because of laziness. In either case not specifying allows him the freedom to interpret the estimate to his benefit, if that is his intention. On page 38 there is an example of an estimate for a central heating/hot water installation. On the face of it this estimate seems to cover all the ingredients required for such an installation. All the bits seem to be there, and they are going to leave it in working order. It will probably do. Now compare it with the detailed estimate on page 39 for the same job. This one gives an initial explanatory paragraph specifying the criteria that affect temperatures. As far as equipment is concerned it states 'supply and install', which clears up any confusion over who supplies materials. It tells you what temperatures are guaranteed for each room, and it gives a lot of technical detail about the system which you may not understand, but armed with that information you could easily find out about it if you wanted to, or subsequently needed to, and of course you can check on the quality of the materials that have been specified. Another advantage of having a lot of specific detail in a written estimate is that, when it comes to comparing different estimates for the same job, you can ensure that they all include exactly the same items of work and the same materials, otherwise the price differences between the estimates will be meaningless. Direct comparison of estimates will be impossible if one specifies cheap materials and the other top quality materials.

Common omissions from estimates

There are several not-so-obvious points to watch for when reading or comparing estimates.

26 September 1990

DOWNTOWN HEATING CONTRACTORS LTD
SIDE STREET
NEWTOWN NT1 2UU

Mr and Mrs Smith
2 The Avenue
Newtown NT2 3ZZ

<u>ESTIMATE</u>

Install central heating and hot water system to the above property.

RADIATORS: Six panel radiators with thermostatic valves to ground and first floors.

BOILER: Wall-mounted balanced flue boiler sited in kitchen.

HOT WATER: Install hot water cylinder and connect to boiler and existing pipework.

CONTROLS: Programmer, room thermostat, cylinder thermostat, pump and motorised valves.

TANK: Feed tank in loft.

GAS: Connect to boiler.

INSULATION: Lag tank and pipework.

To be left tested and in working order

Cost of installation   £2140.00

VAT Reg No: XXX XXXX XX

Traditional grey areas are:

- no mention of how payment is to be made
- no indication of whether rubbish is to be cleared away
- no mention of how long the estimate is valid for

- no mention of guarantees
- start/finish dates not specified
- no mention of continuity of work
- no mention of contractor's insurance
- no mention of whether delays caused by the client will be chargeable
- uncertainty about whether VAT is included.

If there is anything that you don't understand or feel has been left out, ask the contractor to explain and clarify, in writing if necessary. It is almost impossible to cover all aspects of written estimates for different types of work, but generally the more specific detail the better.

Difference between an estimate and a quote

An estimate is a calculated assessment of a job based on time, materials and profit. It is not a fixed price and can be varied, up or down, depending on site conditions, availability of materials and various relevant factors. A quote is a fixed price for a job (but read the small print) to which the contractor is bound, provided the conditions are complied with. Low-priced quotes are sometimes offered as inducements to clients as long as they accept them quickly. This enterprise can help companies and contractors over slack periods.

---

26 September 1990

UPTOWN HEATING CONTRACTORS LTD
MAIN STREET
NEWTOWN NT4 5XX

VAT Reg No: XXX XXXX XX

Mr and Mrs Smith
2 The Avenue
Newtown NT2 3ZZ

ESTIMATE

The proposed installation provides a combined gas-fired central heating and hot water system giving the room temperatures shown below when the external temperature is 30°F and the boiler is operated continuously at 180°F.

BOILER: Supply and install one wall-mounted balanced flue boiler rated at 60,000 btu/h – Robinson Hi-matic DR3, and sited in kitchen.

RADIATORS: Supply and install six steel panel convector radiators, as manufactured by Delrad, each complete with thermostatic and isolating valves, as follows:

Gnd flr front room	1 double panel radiator Temp°F	70
" " dining room	1 " " " "	70
" " kitchen	1 single " " "	65
1st " bathroom	1 " " " "	65
" " bedroom 1	1 double " " "	65
" " " 2	1 " " " "	65

PUMP: Supply and install one variable speed circulating pump with 22mm valves as manufactured by ACS Ltd.

DOMESTIC HOT WATER: Supply and install one 35 gallon Grade 2 indirect foam-lagged copper hot water cylinder and connect to boiler via pumped primary circuit. Connect to existing hot water draw-off pipework.

CONTROLS: Supply and fit one 16-position programmer for independent selection of central heating and/or hot water with two on/off periods per day. Supply and fit one room thermostat and motorised valve to control space heating, and one cylinder thermostat and motorised valve to control hot water temperature. All controls manufactured by ACS Ltd.

GAS: Connect boiler to 22mm metered supply.

TANK: Supply and install one 10/4 gallon PVC feed/expansion tank and connect to mains water and overflow, cold feed and open vent pipework.

INSULATION: Lag all new pipework under ground floor and in loft. Supply and fit one insulating jacket to feed/expansion tank.

OTHER: Supply and fit drain-off points as necessary. Include wiring of all controls.

Fill system and test.
All for the sum of Two Thousand One Hundred and Forty Pounds – £2140.00 plus VAT

An electric power point must be supplied adjacent to the boiler position.
All materials and equipment are guaranteed for one year and workmanship for two years.

This estimate is valid for 30 days only.

> Payment details: XXXXXX
> Insurance details: XXXXXX
> Hourly rate chargeable for additional work: XXXXXX

Deciding which estimates to accept

If a contractor has been strongly recommended, you may decide that you will accept his price no matter what, but mainly to save going through the whole process of trying to find others and then not knowing which to choose. If that is the case your decision is easy and you have avoided one of the headaches. You can use this method for any size of job.

However, in most cases at least three estimates should have been obtained and they will undoubtedly differ in price. The first thing to check is that they all include the same amount of work and the same materials (quality and quantity). If anything is not included or is ambiguous, query it with the contractor concerned and get a revised price. If your estimates were based on drawings and a specification, there should be no problem about what is and isn't included, provided the contractor has interpreted the details correctly. Your decision will then be based on:

- price;
- the contractor's reputation;
- whether (when you met him) he seemed approachable and efficient;
- whether he can meet your start/finish dates.

Whether a contractor is approachable and whether you 'can talk to him' is often an overriding factor for some people when it comes to making the choice because they assume, and sometimes quite rightly so, that if the contractor is not 'user friendly' he will be difficult to work with and unreasonable in his dealings with the client if everything doesn't go his way.

The cheapest estimate isn't always the wisest choice but, unpredictable as these things are, it can often turn out to be the best. You could also look at some of the factors which relate to the prices quoted. For example – size of company; overheads; experience – all have a bearing on how much a contractor charges, so make allowances when comparing estimates. You may want a top quality job, and will therefore go for the contractor with the best reputation. If your funds are limited you will doubtless choose the cheapest.

Be wary of very cheap or very expensive estimates. Cheap estimates could be due to the fact that the contractor is inexperienced, or that his workmanship is shoddy and his standards are generally low, or that he just needs the work – it does happen. Very expensive estimates can be the result of the company concerned being too large for the type of job, the contractor being greedy, or the fact that the contractor concerned has a lot of work in hand and can afford to submit high estimates, knowing that whichever are accepted will be extremely lucrative for him.

If the prices are all roughly the same, cost won't be the most important factor affecting your choice, and you can rely on other criteria.

If a professional is being employed he will be involved in the selection process, and his experience in analysing contractors' estimates and checking their track records will be extremely useful. As a final general comment, there is very little that can predetermine exactly how your particular job will work out, even with the best contractor in the world, as so many factors can influence the way in which things happen.

Contracts

A contract in this context is an agreement to provide work and materials in exchange for payment. For the average job acceptance of the estimate constitutes a contract between you and the person you are employing. Some firms have separate contract documents for you to sign, and these contain clauses which you should read and understand, because they are mainly designed to protect the firm, not you the customer.

Large building projects are more complex and as such usually require one of the recognised forms of building contract. These would be difficult to understand for most people and are normally used where a professional is involved in running your project.

One of the popular forms of contract is described later in the chapter under 'Using a professional and a JCT contract'.

Verbal contracts

Verbal acceptance of an estimate constitutes a contract that is as binding in law as a written contract, although in the event of a dispute verification of exactly what was said on a particular day may be difficult. It is not so much the actual acceptance. of an estimate that is difficult to prove, otherwise the work would not even have been started, but discrepancies over types of material, length of time taken, and what is and isn't extra work (requiring extra payment) which normally lead to ill-feeling and misunderstanding between client and contractor. So verbal contracts are best confined to minor jobs or to people whom you know very well. For example, if the window cleaner quotes £20 for your house and can start immediately, you are unlikely to want a written estimate from him – there would be no need. If you accept his price you have a legal verbal contract – he to clean your windows and you to pay him £20.

You have to decide, and set yourself limits based on how well you know the person working for you, the amount of money involved and the type of job, whether or not to enter into a verbal contract.

Here is a true story:

A man wished to have some extensive building work done on his home. He telephoned a building company who sent a representative to discuss it with him. The representative looked at what needed to be done and told him that the work would cost around £80,000. The client, thinking the cost slightly high but anxious to have the work done quickly, asked the representative when the firm could start the work. He was given a date in the following week. The client, a busy man, told him to go ahead. The representative said that he would need a substantial deposit and, in view of the imminent start date, would require the money immediately (for materials and equipment). They agreed upon a deposit of £30,000, made up of a cheque for £20,000 and £10,000 in cash, the client hoping for a reduction in the final bill by paying partly in cash. The cash and cheque were handed over to the representative who then left. A week after the promised start date the client telephoned the builder's office to ask why his job had not been started. The man he spoke to, the manager of the company, had no knowledge of this (substantial) contract, but said he would speak to the representative when he came in.

On his arrival in the office the representative was questioned and denied all knowledge of the client or his contract. The subsequent discussion between the manager and the client resulted in the furious client contacting his solicitor with the intention of taking legal action against the company but, as no written estimate had been given and no contract had been drawn up, proving that the transaction involving £30,000 had taken place was going to prove difficult. There was nothing in writing. The cheque was the only document involved. The representative had paid the cheque into an account (probably unconnected with him) and had withdrawn the money when it cleared a few days later, pocketing the £10,000 as well, of course. Needless to say, no materials had been ordered and the representative disappeared shortly afterwards.

The moral of this story is, of course, always ask for a detailed estimate and have a proper contract before you part with any money, and do not pay cash over to anyone, at least until materials to the cash value have been deposited on your premises. Also, for a contract of that size, the deposit was large. Smaller payments should have been made in stages, consistent with the amount of work completed.

Maybe the fact that the company involved was of a reasonable size had a bearing on the client's willingness to part with such a large sum of money so readily. Unfortunately, the size of a company does not bear any relationship to the honesty of its employees. There was, in this case, a verbal estimate and a verbal agreement to start the work, but there were no witnesses to, and therefore no proof of, this agreement.

Written contracts
Two types of contract commonly used are:

● time and materials contract
● priced contract.

With a *time and materials* contract you are charged a fixed hourly or daily rate of pay per man plus the cost of materials, equipment hire, professional fees and any other costs relating to the work. There may also be a small percentage added to materials for contractor's profit. This type of contract is normally used where:

- estimating is difficult, perhaps where there are several small jobs of indeterminate length, or perhaps where access is limited to work areas because of daytime occupation, resulting in wasted time;
- the client wishes to organise the job on a piecemeal basis, maybe doing some of the work himself and employing others to help him or to carry out specialist tasks.

The disadvantages of this type of contract are:

- There is no overall price for the contract, so even though you budget and do rough calculations you don't know what the final bill will come to.
- It will probably cost more than you calculated because contractors can afford to take more time when they are being paid by the hour and have a guaranteed fixed income than when they have to meet the financial deadline of a priced job.
- If you have been doing part of the same work as someone you hired, it may be difficult to apportion liability if problems with workmanship or materials occur. For example, if you supply items for installation by contractors (perhaps shower equipment) and there is a subsequent fault in that equipment during the guarantee period, the work involved in replacement would be your responsibility. In other words, the parts would be replaced free of charge by the supplier but you would have to arrange the removal, collection and refitting of them, and this could be expensive with installed items. The contractor was paid a sum of money to fit items supplied by you, and there his responsibility ended (provided they were correctly fitted), whereas if he had *supplied* and installed the equipment he would have been responsible for the guaranteed items.

With a *priced* contract, which is based on an estimate or a quote, you know in advance (barring extras) how much you are going to have to pay. The contractor is careful about pricing because he could be competing with others for the job and if his estimate is too high *or* too low he could lose the contract. Whenever possible, it is better to use a priced contract for work in your home.

Validity of contracts

Before signing a contract it is important to check, among other things, that it is a valid contract.

Whether a contract is actually valid is something that is not always high on the list of priorities amid the preparations to get the work under way, and perhaps would never even come to light unless a dispute resulted in legal proceedings being instituted.

The main factors affecting the validity of a contract are:

- that the objective of the contract does not break the law;
- that the persons entering into the contract must be adult and sane;
- that the contract has not been signed under duress (a cooling-off period is now allowed for some contracts – page 117);
- that consent to the contract has not been obtained by fraudulent means;
- misrepresentation – perhaps where untrue statements are made in order to secure a contract. For example, a contractor could claim to own a large building concern with a high annual turnover, which is eventually proved to be untrue. The client could have engaged him on the strength of this alleged record, and was therefore misled when entering into the contract;
- the contract must be signed in ink.

It is also important for the client to know the status and identity of the person signing the contract, his position in the company, and therefore the validity of his signature. He should also check whether the company is limited, a partnership, foreign-based, a one-man business etc. It could be relevant in the event of a dispute.

Items included in contracts

- **Prime cost sums** (pc sums) are included in the cost of the works to cover the cost of materials which have yet to be decided upon. For example, you may have to choose floor tiles for the conservatory at some later date, so you allow a sum of, say, £500 in the initial costings. If you eventually choose tiles which cost more than that figure, you will have to pay the difference. Likewise, a pc sum can be used to cover the cost of sub-contract work which perhaps hadn't been fully agreed on when the initial specification was drawn up.

  The main contractor would expect to add a percentage for

profit and any work involved in obtaining materials, attendance etc.

- **Attendance** This takes the form of a percentage levied by the main contractor to cover any work he is liable for in 'attending' to the needs of sub-contractors. For example, he may supply plant and equipment and rubbish skips for their use. He could also be liable for making good to walls, floors and ceilings after sub-contractors have finished. His charge for this service could be between 10 and 15 per cent of the sub-contract cost.
- **Provisional sums** These relate to work which couldn't be assessed properly at the time the original costings were done. For example, roof timbers couldn't be inspected as there was no access, but they were known to be in need of replacement. Once the main contractor started the job he could expose the roof and an estimate could be obtained

Schedules

A schedule is a list of the various sections of the work which have been estimated for on a particular job. It can include the cost of each section and the time allowed. On some contracts it would be used to prepare a works programme (pages 90–91). It can also be a list of materials and the sums allowed for their purchase.

Invoices

An invoice is a bill, or account, for payment either as a deposit or at any stage of the work you are having done.

For a small job you would probably just get one – when the job was finished. Other jobs would need two – one at the start and one at the finish. On large jobs the contractor would require payment at regular intervals (stage payments) and would present invoices at monthly or other previously agreed intervals. You are normally allowed a certain time to settle invoiced accounts, and 14 days would not be unreasonable. In the case of a deposit your job would not be started until you had paid, of course.

An invoice can also be a notification of advice of despatch of goods, including cost and quantity. Two typical invoices are shown on pages 48 and 49. You should always get an invoice before making a payment.

Invoice for a small job

Bill's Tiles   2 February 1990
6 High Street
London XX3 1YY

VAT Reg No: **XXX XXXX XX**

Mrs Jones
Acacia Road
London YY2 4XX

<u>INVOICE</u>

Tiling of kitchen floor as per our estimate dated 10 January 1990

Estimate	£200.00
Additional work:	
Refix bathroom tiles	£ 30.00
Subtotal	£230.00
VAT at 15%	£ 34.50
Total	£264.50

Please settle this account within fourteen days

W. Smith

Note the usual request stating payment-by date, giving you time to 'road-test' the work and report any defects.

Large job – intermediate or 'stage payment' invoice

This is an example of the type of invoice that would be presented to the client where a JCT contract (see page 52) was not used, retention sums were not being deducted, and the builder had prepared a specification and schedule.

---

3 April 1990

Client: P. Smith, 17 High Street, Anytown AT1 2XX

Builder: XXXXX & Son, Unit 3, Trading Estate, Anytown AT3 4YY

Contract: New rear extension, 17 High Street, Anytown AT1 2XX

<u>INVOICE NO 3</u>

Work completed to date:

   Item 1.7 – 40%

   Item 1.9 – 25%

   Item 3.5 – 90%

   Item 3.6 – 70%

   Item 4.4 – 65%

Additional work to date: none

Contract sum	£14,853.00
Previous payments	£ 6,200.00
Payment requested this invoice	£ 3,540.00
VAT at 15%	£ 531.00
Total	£ 4,071.00

per pro XXXX & Son

VAT Reg No: XXX XXXX XX

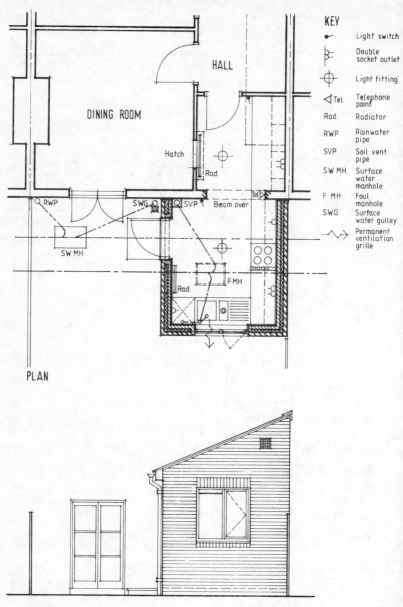

KEY

●	Light switch
	Double socket outlet
	Light fitting
◁Tel.	Telephone point
Rad.	Radiator
RWP	Rainwater pipe
SVP	Soil vent pipe
SW MH	Surface water manhole
F MH	Foul manhole
SWG	Surface water gulley
	Permanent ventilation grille

HALL

DINING ROOM

Hatch

Rad.

RWP

SWG

SVP

Beam over

Tel

SW MH

FMH

Rad.

PLAN

ELEVATION

0   1   2   3M

Figure 6.1 *Plan and elevation*

Drawings

If your job requires drawings (or plans) these will be provided by an architect or a draughtsman. Sometimes drawings are required just for local authority approval of the work you intend to carry out, in which case they must be submitted before work starts. Your local council will advise when these are needed and how much detail needs to be shown. In most cases drawings are produced primarily for the contractor or installer to work to and contain the necessary information to enable him to carry out the work to the intended design. However, being able to understand what they mean could be extremely useful to the client, especially for monitoring what is happening in his house, and visualising how the finished job will look.

'Design' drawings are those produced initially to indicate the intended layout and show proposed schemes. 'Working' drawings are those produced when the layout has been finalised, and these are the ones that contractors work to.

The two basic types of drawing are *plan* and *elevation*. A plan is a view from above – looking down at the floor. An elevation is a vertical view. Examples of both types of drawings are shown opposite, with explanations. Most drawings for domestic contracts would be to the scale of 1:50, with some at the larger scale of 1:20, where it was necessary to show greater detail – for example, in a kitchen where services and appliances are concentrated. To read a drawing easily it is worthwhile investing in a scale rule, as this facilitates converting drawing measurements to real size.

Explanations of the drawings

The drawings opposite show a rear extension to a house.

Plan: The type of construction shown is an outer wall of brick and an inner wall of blockwork (large lightweight concrete blocks).

The cavity between the two is shown filled with insulation material. The sink unit is shown in front of the window and the cooker on the right-hand side (the four rings).

Two sets of drainage and manholes are shown, one for foul, one for surface water although in some areas of the country these are combined. The manhole in the kitchen is of 'double seal' construction. This type is used inside a property. The door into the garden is shown on the left-hand side.

Elevation: This view shows the back of the extension. The dotted line on the window indicates the opening side.

The large dotted line at the bottom of the brickwork indicates the position of the damp proof course.

Air brick – top right.

Rainwater pipe – to the left of the extension.

Using a professional and a JCT contract

If you are using a professional to manage a large project on your home, he may suggest one of the recognised forms of contract used for building works. There are several of these that relate to the type of work carried out on domestic properties. A popular one, and the one described here, is that produced by the Joint Contracts Tribunal (JCT). This tribunal is composed of a panel of representatives from the RIBA, RICS, other professional bodies, and the contracting industry.

JCT contracts

Three forms of JCT contract are commonly used in the United Kingdom. They are:

- the standard form of contract (JCT 80)
- the intermediate form of contract (IFC 84)
- the agreement for minor building works (MW 80)
  (The numbers relate to the year the form of the contract was introduced.)

The standard form of the contract is used for large (mainly commercial or industrial) projects up to any size or value, and is not suitable for small-scale domestic works.

The intermediate form is recommended for contracts of up to £280,000 (1987 prices) and again is unsuitable except for large domestic works.

The agreement for minor building works (part of which is shown opposite) is recommended for contracts of up to £70,000 (1987 prices) and is the one generally used for domestic works. It is also the best as far as the client is concerned, being the simplest to interpret.

The upper limits for contract sums are only a guide, and can be exceeded if required. The more accurate criteria relied upon to determine which form of contract is used relate to the complexity

JCT　**Agreement for Minor Building Works**

This Agreement is made the_____day of_____19_____

between_____

of_____
(hereinafter called 'the Employer')

of the one part AND_____

of (or whose registered office is at)_____

_____

(hereinafter called 'the Contractor') of the other part.

Whereas

Recitals

1st　the Employer wishes the following work_____

_____

_____

(hereinafter called "the Works") to be carried out under the direction of

_____

(hereinafter called "the Architect/the Contract Administrator") [a] and has caused drawings numbered
(hereinafter called "the Contract Drawings") [b] and/or a Specification (hereinafter called "the Contract Specification") [b] and/or schedules [b] (which documents are together with the Conditions annexed hereto hereinafter called "the Contract Documents") showing and describing the works to be prepared and which are attached to this Agreement;

2nd　the Contractor has priced the Specification [b] or the schedules [b] or provided a schedule of rates [b];

3rd　the Contract Documents have been signed by or on behalf of the parties hereto;

4th　[b] the quantity surveyor appointed in connection with this contract shall mean

_____

or in the event of his death or ceasing to be the quantity surveyor for this purpose such other person as the Employer nominates for that purpose;

5th　[b-1] the Employer wishes that a guarantee/warranty scheme shall apply in respect of the Works to be carried out under this Agreement and that the Recitals, Articles and Conditions shall therefore have effect as modified by the amendments in Part E, Section_____[b-2], of the Supplementary Memorandum to the Agreement for Minor Building Works.

[a] Where the person named is entitled to the use of the name 'Architect' under and in accordance with the Architect's (Registration) Acts 1931 to 1969 delete 'the Contract Administrator': in all other cases delete 'Architect'. Where 'Architect' is deleted the expression 'Architect' shall be deemed to have been deleted throughout this Agreement; where 'the Contract Administrator' is deleted the expression 'the Contract Administrator' shall be deemed to have been deleted throughout this Agreement.	[b] Delete as appropriate. [b-1] Insert reference number of the applicable section. [b-2] If fifth recital not deleted insert reference number of the applicable section.

MW 1989

Reproduced by permission of the copyright holders, RIBA Publications Limited.

of the works and how long the job will take.

The contracts contain standard clauses defining under what conditions the work is to be carried out. Additional clauses can be added to suit particular jobs or special requirements. They are complex documents and as such are rarely used for small jobs.

Where a JCT contract is used, the job would normally be run by a professional, although a client with sufficient knowledge of building works *could* run it himself. Understanding the details and the correct procedure, though, could be difficult and could leave an inexperienced person wishing that he'd never taken it on.

Almost inevitably, if a contractor prices a job based on a JCT contract the estimate will be higher than if it wasn't used. The reasons are that the contractor is strictly governed by the rules of the contract, much more so than with a straightforward (non-JCT) written contract, which dictate how he must carry out the job, the dates he must keep to and finish by, when he gets paid and the financial penalties he could be liable for. It also gives the client the right, via his agent (the professional), to reject work not in accordance with the specification. The client, although paying more for his job than if the JCT contract was not used, is protected by its provisions, especially as far as making payments is concerned, having proper insurance cover, and having the tried and tested legal and contractual obligations tied up in one document. The client is also liable for architect's and other professional's fees, of course, but the onerous task of setting up, organising and running the contract is put into expert hands, and with a large job that service is worth having.

The way that the 'minor works' agreement operates is as follows:

- Contract documents are prepared. In simple form these consist of general preliminaries, drawings and specifications and the contract document itself.
- General preliminaries are concerned with any special requirements and conditions that relate to the contract. For example: 'Working hours must be confined to weekdays between 8 am and 6 pm', 'All carpets are to be taken up in working areas and replaced on completion', 'All rubbish and debris is to be removed daily – builder's skips are not to be sited at the front of the property.'

Of course, the more conditions that are imposed the more

expensive the job will be. You should discuss with your professional what is normal and reasonable for the type of job that is being undertaken. Tying up the contract too tightly will make the contractor's working conditions difficult, and could affect his overall performance.

- Drawings and specifications are sent to the contractors who have been invited to tender (estimate).
- Drawings and specifications are sent to the sub-contractors and specialist contractors who have been invited to tender. (Several estimates can be obtained for the main and each of the sub-contracts. These are called competitive tenders.)
- Tenderers are given a date by which their estimates must be returned, and when they are all received the decision about which ones to accept is taken. This decision depends on how near the estimates come to the original costs calculated by the professional, and in consultation with the client. If some or all of the estimates are too high it may be necessary to go out to tender again, or re-design or reduce the proposed works. This will generally delay the start of the job, but it is a choice between accepting a delay or paying a higher price. If re-tendering, do not forget that inflation can cause prices to rise anyway in the period during which new estimates are obtained.
- The contracts are signed and work commences according to the site programme.
- The architect or other professional makes regular visits to assess progress and to determine whether drawings and specifications are being adhered to. He will also notify the client of any additional costs. If any additional work or a variation to the contract is required, an 'Architect's Instruction' (AI) (see page 56) is issued. This is an order to the contractor(s) to carry out the work, and ensures that he gets paid for it. Verbal instructions should be avoided, and the client should not instruct the contractors himself.
- Valuations of 'work completed to date' are made at regular intervals agreed in advance (usually once a month). The valuations include the work of all contractors employed on the site. If a quantity surveyor has been used he will prepare the valuations, which will include (a) the value of the work executed, and (b) the value of materials on site (and sometimes off site).
- The architect issues an *interim certificate* following each

---

Architect:
address:

Architect's instruction

Employer:
address:

Job reference:

Serial No:

Issue date:

Contractor:
address:

Works:
situated at:

Under the terms of the Contract dated _____ I/We issue the following instructions.

Where applicable the Contract Sum will be adjusted in accordance with the terms of the relevant Condition.

Instructions	Office use: Approx costs
	£ omit £ add

Signed _____ Architect

Amount of Contract Sum	£	
± Approximate value of previous instructions	£	
	£	
± Approximate value of this instruction	£	
Approximate adjusted total	£	

Original to:	Copies to:		Nominated Sub-Contractors:	
☐ Contractor	☐ Employer	☐ Structural Consultant	☐ _____	☐ _____
	☐ Quantity Surveyor	☐ Services Consultant	☐ _____	☐ _____
	☐ Clerk of Works	☐ Electrical Consultant	☐ _____	☐ Site

© RIBA Publications Ltd 1982

Reproduced by permission of the copyright holders, RIBA Publications Limited.

valuation, which specifies the amount of money to be released by the client, who then has 14 days (standard) from the valuation date to make the payment. Failure to pay within the agreed time is grounds for certain action by the contractor (see page 108). Deductions are made for 'retention'. This is a sum of money, usually 5 per cent, owed to the contractor but retained by the client. Half of it is released to the contractor when the work is complete (see below), and the remainder upon completion of the defects schedule drafted by the architect at the end of the 'defects liability period' (see below).

- 'Practical completion' means that the job has effectively come to an end. After the 'snagging lists' (see page 96) have been issued and their requirements dealt with, the architect has to make the decision that the job is ready for the issue of a *certificate of practical completion* (see page 58). Once this happens the main and sub-contractors benefit considerably, because from that date:

  (a) the final valuation is started;
  (b) half of the retention sum held by the client is due for release;
  (c) the contractors' liability for insurance and liquidated damages ceases.

  It is also the start of the *defects liability period*.

- A *final certificate*. Within the specified time, usually three months from the date of practical completion, the contractor has to supply all the relevant information, invoices, accounts and any other documentation, including sub-contractors' accounts, necessary for the calculation of the final certificate. This certificate then becomes due within 28 days, subject to the making good of any defects. It is a statement of the final account of the job, and indicates the amounts previously certified, the amounts of any variations/additions/deletions to the contract, and the amount of the balance due, which then becomes payable within the specified time, unless any legal or arbitration proceedings have been started by either party.

- After the *defects liability period* (usually six months or one year) has ended, the contractor is required to make good any defects which relate to his work. He is not liable for any work which was the responsibility of the client. After the expiry of the defects

Issued by:
address:

Employer:
address:

Contractor:
address:

Works:
Situated at:

Contract dated:

Certificate of

**Practical
Completion**

of the Works

Serial no:

Job reference:

Issue date:

Under the terms of the above mentioned Contract,

I/We certify that Practical Completion of the Works was achieved on:

_____ 19_____

To be signed by or for
the issuer named
above

Signed_____

The Defects Liability Period will therefore end on:

_____ 19_____

Distribution	Original to:	Duplicate to:	Copies to:	
	☐ Employer	☐ Contractor	☐ Quantity Surveyor	☐ Services Engineer
		☐ Nominated Sub-Contractors	☐ Structural Engineer	☐ File

(c) 1985 RIBA Publications Ltd

Reproduced by permission of the copyright holders, RIBA Publications
Limited.

liability period, the remainder of the retention sum becomes due to the contractor.

Sub-contractors

Sub-contractors – so called because they are usually *under* the main contractor – are normally specialists, ie electricians, roofers etc. The main contractor will arrange the necessary sub-contractors for his jobs, and will try to use those known to him, mainly because he will be directly responsible for ensuring that they do the specified work in the time allowed. He will also be responsible for paying them.

On some jobs the client or the professional will 'nominate' or name a sub-contractor that he wishes to be used, in which case the main contractor is still responsible for his work and his payment. The JCT minor works agreement does not provide for nominated sub-contractors, but this can be overcome by inserting a clause in the contract.

It is usual for the main contractor to expect a 'discount', normally $2\frac{1}{2}$ per cent on the sub-contract price, for every sub-contractor he is responsible for.

If the client employs a specialist contractor directly for work connected with a contract being run by a main contractor, the specialist contractor would be answerable to the client only, and would not come under the control of the main contractor. The main contractor could, however, have a claim against the client if his contract was adversely affected by the specialist. On most jobs the client would not have to bother himself with details of how the system works, but it can be useful to know.

Prime cost and provisional sums

Provision is made for the inclusion of these in the JCT MW 80 contract, and they have been described earlier in this chapter (see page 46).

Extensions of time

A certificate for extension of time can be issued by the architect to extend the finishing date of the contract where either additional works are required or there are unavoidable delays, eg inclement weather; late information. The contractor is sometimes allowed to charge an additional amount for overheads and profit, depending upon the reason for the extension.

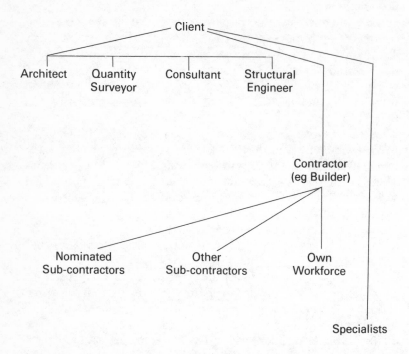

Figure 6.2 *An example of how various professionals and contractors are employed. The size and/or complexity of the contract would normally determine how many were used.*

The client employs the architect and the contractor. Other professionals can be recommended to the client by the architect to cover areas of work not familiar to him. Whether or not an architect is used, the contractor is employed directly by the client. The contractor can do all the work himself with his own employees, or call in other contractors for specialist jobs (eg roofing, heating), in which case he becomes the main contractor, and the specialists are then sub-contractors. Specialists can also be employed directly by the client, in which case the main contractor is not responsible for them. The architect tends to co-ordinate the activities of the other professionals. A surveyor could be employed instead of an architect.

Chapter 7

Charges, Fees and Methods of Payment

It is difficult for the average householder to know exactly what to expect when asking about charges for work in the home. Some rough idea of the cost of particular jobs and pay rates can be formed by chats with neighbours and friends, or gleaned from newspaper advertisements, but charges rise regularly so you should make sure that you know what the current rates are before budgeting your job.

Specialist trades

These include:

- bricklayer
- carpenter
- electrician
- plumber
- plasterer.

Employing these tradesmen on an hourly or daily basis would involve typical charges of between £7 and £15 per hour per man (1989 prices). The average day would be between 8 and 10 hours.

The so-called 'wet trades', like plastering, are normally the most expensive, and sometimes two people are needed to carry out the work. Obviously, materials would have to be added to these charges, as well as VAT, if the person is registered. If you go to a builder who then supplies a specialist tradesman, you would expect to pay an additional amount to cover his profit.

Jobs which only take up part of the day are usually relatively more expensive and you may be charged for the whole day even though the job is finished by 3 o'clock. This is because it is then too late for the tradesman to start another job at another address, and by not charging for the full day he would be out of pocket.

Others

This general heading includes semi-skilled and unskilled people who will take on a variety of jobs. Handymen, youngsters and pensioners will often be able to do some of the same jobs as specialists, although not necessarily to the same standard. Odd jobs and gardening jobs would also come into this category.

Depending on the type of job, you can expect to pay between £2 and £12 per hour per person (1989 prices) and are less likely to have to pay VAT.

Call-out charges

Call-out charges are normally fixed and cover an initial period for a small job or emergency work. The charges are usually higher than average rates of pay because they include the time spent travelling and picking up spare parts, and cover the cost of using any specialist equipment (eg for drain clearing). They also have to cover the convenience and mobility of the service.

A typical call-out charge would be around £25 plus any materials and VAT (1989 prices), which would cover the first hour or half-hour, with a lower rate for subsequent periods. Charges tend to be higher outside normal working hours.

- **Gas/electricity emergency call-outs**. If there is a fault between your meter and the main supply in the road, a call-out is usually free. If the reason for the call-out is connected with any other part of your supply, a charge is payable.
- **Water emergency call-outs**. From the water main in the street up to the stopcock in the pavement or garden of your property is the responsibility of the water authority. From that stopcock up to and including your property, the pipework is your responsibility and a call-out charge would normally be levied for any work associated with it. Charges for all three services vary between £15 and £35 plus VAT, more outside normal working hours.

Overtime

Overtime rates vary enormously. Building firms and large contractors are likely to have fixed rates for their employees who work more than a standard day. A time-and-a-half method is sometimes used. This means that you are charged the hourly rate plus half the hourly rate for every hour or part of an hour of overtime worked.

With individuals it is often a matter for their own judgement, depending on how late they have worked, the site conditions etc, and they may just add a nominal sum to the final bill.

How professionals charge

Both the RIBA and the RICS issue guidelines relating to the fees that their members should charge. These guidelines will help you to work out the overall costs involved in a particular job if you intend using a professional.

Professionals can charge a lump sum for their part in a project, an hourly rate, or a percentage of the total construction costs. The size of the job and the degree of involvement of the professional could have a bearing on which method is adopted. If the hourly rate method is to be used, you would be wise to get some idea of how much time the professional thinks he will need to spend on your project.

If you want to use a professional to design, organise and run the whole project for you, it is worth doing some research. See page 26 for details of RIBA publications.

Under the RIBA system a proportion of the architect's fee is payable at clearly defined work stages. These are:

Work stages

A and B	Discussion, assessment, feasibility and advice.
C and D	Outline proposals, estimate of costs, a design of the scheme and planning applications.
E	Detailed design of the scheme, decisions about specialists and sub-contractors and applications for approval under building acts.
F and G	Production information is prepared, including drawings, schedules and specifications for materials and workmanship. At this stage all the necessary information is available for a contractor to prepare a tender.
H, J, K, L	These sections cover the period from going out to tender until the completion of the project. They include getting the tenders and advising on them

once submitted; advice on the appointment of the contractor, and arranging for the signing of the contract; supervising the contract and making regular site visits; reporting to the client; administering the project until completion.

This is an outline of the basic services that are provided, which should be discussed in detail with your professional.

Fees are paid in relation to the work stages completed and the recommended percentages are as follows:

Work stage	Proportion of fee %	Cumulative total %
C and D	35	35
E	20	55
F and G	20	75
H, J, K, L	25	100

Any additional work would probably be charged at an hourly rate, and if your project required other professional services, eg a structural engineer, you would be liable for those fees as well. You would also be liable for any statutory fees in respect of planning or building regulations. Other costs would include expenses and disbursements, and VAT.

You could, if you wanted, pay for 'partial services' by your professional, and manage the remainder of the project yourself, depending on your confidence and ability, and, of course, on how much money you wanted to spend. An architect could provide drawings, specifications and recommend contractors, for example, and you could supervise the running of the project.

Additional/unexpected charges

Having obtained an estimate or quote, do not fall into the trap of thinking that the price automatically covers everything.

For example, 'install and wire one external light fitting to porch' does not say whether the cost of the light fitting and the cable are included. In other words the price quoted may be just for labour. To the unsuspecting client, thinking he has accepted an estimate for the complete job, the cost of materials can represent a significant additional expense which he has not anticipated.

Although this is a simple example, it is always wise to check on what is and what is not included; if it is still ambiguous, have a written explanation.

The following list gives some examples of how estimates and charges do not always cover everything.

- **Travelling time** – not necessarily an extra charge, but the day you are paying for could start when the contractor leaves his home, not when he arrives at your house. This means a shorter working day and a longer job. If you are paying an hourly rate, the additional cost could be significant. The problem normally arises when the contractor lives some distance away.

- **Price rises** – make sure that your estimate is valid for a certain period; a month would be reasonable, within which time you can accept the price quoted. If there is no time limit for acceptance, or you accept outside the specified time, the price may rise to cover increased material and/or labour costs.

- **Insurance** – Make sure that the values of your building and contents insurances are up to date, especially when having major works carried out in your home. Sometimes you are required to insure the works anyway. (See Chapter 8.)

- **Servicing/guarantees** – not really an additional cost, but check whether guarantees and warranties exist for equipment and installed items and whether both parts and labour are included, how much servicing will cost and who will do it. Some equipment can only be serviced by the manufacturers who may have a lengthy, and therefore expensive, journey to get to your home. Certain items of equipment carry no guarantees (eg some imported goods) and if, as sometimes happens, there is no back-up or service organisation, the only recourse in the event of a breakdown would be replacement with another product. This has been known to happen and has proved very expensive for the client.

- **VAT** – an estimate or contract should indicate whether VAT is to be charged. The total sum quoted would not normally include VAT, so it is to be added. Some small businesses and individuals are not VAT registered so it does not go on to the bill. If in doubt about whether a contractor is VAT registered, check on whether his registration number appears on his bill, and if you are still not satisfied you can telephone your local Customs and Excise office (listed in the phone book) for advice.

- **Rubbish** – a large job would normally include the clearance of rubbish and debris by the contractor, but small jobs often result in the client being left with packing cases, old equipment, dismantled items etc, and he has to pay to have them taken away.
- **Attendant work** – a client is sometimes obliged to arrange to have certain work carried out prior to and/or subsequent to a particular contract. For example, having a new kitchen installed may require the demolition of a chimney breast, which would have to be done by a builder, and afterwards the making-good and decoration. Allowance should always be made for attendant work when obtaining estimates, including any which may involve gas, electricity or water authorities.
- **Surveys** – some companies may charge a survey fee (sometimes ostensibly an estimating fee) to look at your property in order to give an estimate.
- **Deposits** – some companies require quite substantial deposits when you place an order with them, even though the actual work may be months away. Some even require the whole amount in advance. This exercise means that your money is earning interest in their bank account – not yours.

Methods of payment

- **Small jobs** – (under £100) would normally be settled upon completion, without a deposit.
- **Average jobs** – the higher the value of the job, the more likely it is that the contractor will need some initial payment to enable him to buy materials and provide him with some income. There may be a delay in obtaining the final payment (initial payments are always more forthcoming from clients than final payments), so the wise contractor makes sure that he gets some money 'up front'. Although the contractor may ask for it, the client should avoid paying a large initial payment, unless there are lots of materials already ordered or on the premises.
- **Large jobs** – where the contract will extend to several months an agreement should be made between client and contractor for payments at regular intervals (eg every four weeks). These are called *stage payments* and the amount to be paid would depend on an assessment of how much work had been completed at the stage payment date. This assessment is called a valuation. It is

important not to pay too much at each stage of the job, and when the final payment becomes due it is important to check that everything is in order before handing over the money (see also page 95). For a job run by a professional, see page 52.

- **Cash payments** – some contractors will ask for payment in cash, especially for small jobs. The reasons include:
  - *security* – clients' cheques could bounce;
  - *the need to buy materials* where the contractor's cheques are not accepted;
  - *accepting cheques* for lots of small jobs would mean frequent (time-wasting) trips to the bank.

Payment in advance

Some companies, especially fitted kitchen installers and double glazing contractors, require the total payment for the job before starting work or delivering any materials to the site. You would be wise to avoid these organisations if at all possible, because once they have your money you have no effective control over the quality of the installation or how quickly it is done. They can offer all sorts of excuses for not meeting promised starting dates – 'the units were ordered last April but the suppliers have had problems', or 'a lot of people are off sick at the moment'. In fact they can say what they like, and if you ask for your money back and your requests are ignored, your only recourse is to the courts.

Also, if the company you have paid closes down and goes into liquidation, it is unlikely that you will ever see your money again.

Sometimes you have no choice about advance payment. The gas, water and electricity authorities can charge in this way, and as they are monopolies there is no alternative.

Receipts and cheque payments

No matter what the job, always ask for a receipt for every payment. A cheque is a form of receipt in itself as payment can be traced, but do not leave cheques open, or made out to 'pay bearer' or 'pay cash'. Put the contractor's name, or company name, on to a crossed cheque and write 'A/C payee only' between the crossed lines. This ensures that the cheque is paid into the correct account, and cannot be spirited away by anyone. Cheque fraud is increasing and you stand to lose a lot of money if your sizeable cheque to a contractor is not paid for any reason, and goes astray – you probably won't get your job finished either.

On jobs that are run by a professional, using a recognised form of contract with proper documentation will mean that payments are correctly receipted.

Calculating costs yourself

If you want a good idea of what a particular job will cost before getting estimates, you can make your own calculations by breaking it down into labour, materials, equipment and profit. This is obviously much easier with a small job, but the principle is the same for larger jobs.

Take a job such as painting and decorating a room. Make a list as follows:

Hire of wallpaper stripper	£ 10
10 rolls of lining paper	£ 15
10 rolls of patterned paper	£ 60
5 litres of white emulsion (ceiling)	£ 7
2 litres of white undercoat	£ 8
2 litres of white gloss paint	£ 10
Miscellaneous items – brushes, paste, white spirit etc	£ 15
Labour – one man for three days, including use of own equipment and profit	£320
Total	£445

Don't forget VAT.

Before you can assemble a list like this you will have to go to your local DIY shop or builders merchant, work out the coverage of paint and wallpaper (allowing 10 per cent waste), find out the cost of materials and equipment hire and then enquire about decorators' charges.

Other fees and costs

- **District Surveyor** (also called Building Inspector or Building Control Officer). There is a scale of fees, set by the Department of the Environment (DOE), which relates to the cost of the project being undertaken. The minimum fee is £18.40 (1989 prices).

- **Local authority planning department**. Fees for planning approval do not vary according to the cost of the project, but there are different fixed amounts payable, depending on the type of project (eg extension, loft conversion etc).
- **Gas, electricity and water authorities**. Various fees and charges relate to work connected with these services, eg re-siting a gas meter, installing a new water main. The authority concerned will provide an estimate for the particular work involved.
- **Rubbish clearance/skips**. Skips (rubbish containers) cost about £60 (1989 prices) each time you use one, and having rubbish cleared by a contractor with a truck will cost about the same.
- **Insurance**. See Chapter 8.

Some or all of these costs may be included in the sum that you pay your contractor, but if you are organising and running your own job you must allow for them.

Insurance

One of the most important considerations when having work done on your property is insurance. There are various types of insurance which will protect you and your property, some which contractors should have, and some which you should arrange yourself.

When having anyone in to work for you it is important to remember that the size of the job being carried out is irrelevant as far as the need for insurance is concerned. It is as possible to cause £10,000 worth of damage as a result of an hour's work as it is during a six-month contract. Many people already have home insurance policies which may protect them while contractors are being employed, to some degree at least. The Association of British Insurers (ABI) provides comprehensive advice on all aspects of insurance.

The following is a general guide to the relevant types of insurance available. Details can differ from company to company.

Householders' insurance

- **Buildings insurance** – covers the structure and permanent fixtures and fittings, eg kitchen and bathroom fixtures, and decorations. Most policies can be extended to provide cover for 'alternative accommodation' should your property be uninhabitable because of damage by an insured risk. Also covered under this type of insurance are 'underground service pipes and cables', eg gas, electricity, water and drainage services.
- **Contents insurance**. These policies generally cover non-fixtures, eg personal belongings and other household items including valuables. If items like this are at risk while work is going on, it is worth making sure that you are fully covered.
- **Property owners' liability insurance**. If you own your property this insurance covers you in the event of your injuring someone

or damaging his property. This type of cover would be beneficial for people who carry out their own home improvements, as in the case, for example, of a neighbouring property being damaged by your actions.

With buildings insurance make sure that you have the correct level of cover, based on current rebuilding costs and including all permanent fixtures and fittings (eg double glazing and central heating). Advice about these costs can be obtained from your insurance company or a surveyor, and remember that rebuilding costs do not necessarily bear any relation to the market value of your property. All policies have some exclusions and limits. Exclusions (damage not covered by the policy) can differ depending on the policy, so always check with your insurance company before getting estimates and employing contractors to do repair work which you thought was covered by insurance because you might end up paying for damage yourself. Favourite exclusions include:

- *Force majeure* (act of God)
- storm or flood to certain parts of the property
- frost.

Some policies are liable to 'excess'. An excess is an amount that you have to pay from your own pocket towards the cost of each claim. It can sometimes be quite substantial, especially when relating to subsidence, so if subsidence forms part of the claim you are making to pay for building work, make sure that you have the excess in the bank.

Contractors' insurance

It is less likely that the odd-job man you employ once in a while will have the comprehensive insurance cover accepted as standard by established contracting and building companies. That is one good reason for having your own insurance. However, before you accept an estimate from a company or a small concern, it is in your interest to ask what kind of insurance cover it has, and ask to see evidence if necessary. If you employ someone who does not have insurance, and he damages your or your neighbour's property, and refuses to rectify the damage, your only recourse against him would be legal action, and if he doesn't have any assets you would be wasting your time. Also, your neighbour could have a claim against you.

There are various types of contractor's insurance but the ones that mainly affect the client are:

- **public liability insurance**. This is necessary because contractors carry out the majority of their work in and on other people's premises. This insurance, as its title implies, is there to protect the public, or more specifically any person affected by the work being undertaken, and property damaged by the contractor or his workforce. A main contractor is also responsible for sub-contractors, although they should have their own insurance.

   Examples of incidents that would be covered by this type of insurance are:

   - a builder digs a hole outside your property to connect a drainage pipe and a passer-by falls into it and breaks a leg.
   - a contractor severs a buried water pipe and causes flood damage to your property.

   Obviously the contractor is only liable for damage or injury for which he is responsible. If a chimney pot falls off and damages the roof while he is laying a new basement floor, he cannot be expected to claim on his policy. If, on the other hand, he is partly responsible, there may have to be a joint claim (client and contractor).

   Contractors carry public liability insurance not only to protect the customer, but themselves as well in the event of claims which would otherwise bankrupt them. If a professional is running your job, he should specify that contractors have the correct level of cover.

- **all-risks insurance.** This covers a variety of 'perils' which could befall the contractor. All-risks in this context means nearly all risks, as all policies have exclusions. It protects the premises, materials, machinery, equipment, plant etc of the contractor against damage, theft and vandalism.

The basic difference between public liability and all-risks is that one protects the client and the other the contractor. However, it is certainly in the client's interest that the contractor he employs has all-risks insurance, especially for medium to large jobs. If you are using a professional, he can advise.

The following is an example of how the client can be affected by the contractor not having all-risks insurance:

> A builder has a large amount of equipment and materials stolen from the client's premises. The client is not responsible and the public liability insurance does not cover theft. For the builder to continue with the job he would have to re-purchase the stolen items. The costs involved could make continuation of the job pointless, as whatever was subsequently earned would only go towards paying for the stolen items, not profit for the builder. He may, therefore, decide to ditch the whole contract or, if the losses are very heavy, declare himself bankrupt. In either case the client loses out.

The example illustrates what *can* happen in a fairly extreme case, but most contracts stay the course despite small-scale theft and other setbacks.

Professional indemnity insurance

Architects, surveyors, engineers and other professionals have policies tailored to their particular needs. This insurance is designed to protect them in the event of claims for negligence.

JCT contracts

All three forms of the JCT contract have clauses relating to insurance. The 'minor works' form is the one normally used for domestic contracts, and your professional can explain the details of this, the levels of cover needed and any special requirements. In broad terms the 'minor works' contract covers:

- injury to persons or property
- insurance of the works (new and existing structures)
- remedies for failure to insure
- indemnities (injury to persons or property).

The insurance of the works includes 'special perils', eg explosion, fire, storm, flood etc. The client may be required to insure the existing structure, with the contractor responsible for new works. Insurance must be in force before the contractor arrives on site, and must be maintained until the issue of the certificate of practical completion (see Chapter 6).

Your professional will advise on insurance requirements for your particular project.

Summary

- For small jobs (by handymen, casual workers, part-timers), make sure you have your own insurance.
- If the work you are having done affects neighbouring property, make sure that any insurance cover protects them as well.
- If your job is particularly large or expensive, or requires special cover (perhaps the area you live in is liable to flooding), make certain that the insurer knows about it in advance.
- Make sure that any claim that is made on a policy includes both the main damage and any effects of it, eg repairs to a damaged roof *and* any internal damage.
- Ask to see details of a contractor's insurance, if necessary.
- Make sure that insurance cover is in force *before* work starts.
- JCT contracts make provision for insurance – check details with your professional and insurance company.

Chapter 9
Local Authority Requirements

When you carry out certain types of work on your home you will
have to approach your local authority in relation to:

- planning permission
- building regulations.

Don't be tempted to ignore the rules, thinking that 'no one will find
out', as you could be forced to dismantle the work you have just
paid to have done, especially if neighbours object to an extension
to your property, for example.

Planning permission

Planning applications are dealt with by the planning department of
your local authority and the planning officer is the person to
contact if you need information or advice on whether permission
is required for the work you intend to have done. The application
and approval (or refusal) procedure can take several months, so
you should make sure that you start it well in advance of the time
that you actually want to do the work.

Certain types of work are called 'permitted developments', and
planning permission is not normally required for work in this
category unless your house is in a 'conservation area' or is a 'listed
building'.

Conservation areas are declared by the local council when it
wishes to retain the character and amenities of an area, and control
the development within it. Buildings are listed because they have
some architectural or historical merit, and if you want to alter
them in any way approval must be sought from the listed buildings
authority. You can check on whether your house is listed by
contacting their office (page 138).

The rules relating to flats and maisonettes are different and you should seek advice from your planning department.

Permitted developments

Under current legislation permitted developments are:

Extensions to the property. These are permitted as long as they are not more than 10 per cent or 50 cubic metres of the cubic volume of a terraced house, and 15 per cent or 70 cubic metres of the cubic volume of a detached or semi-detached house. The maximum for both types of property is 115 cubic metres. There are certain conditions attached to these limits, and they include:

- a maximum height of four metres if within two metres of a boundary;
- the extension must not be higher than the house itself;
- the extension must not be built nearer the public highway than the house itself, or within 20 metres, whichever is the nearer.

Loft conversions. These are allowed when not more than 40 cubic metres for a terraced house, and 50 cubic metres for a detached or semi-detached house. The calculation must take into account the totals permitted (as above) ie you cannot have both roof and rear extensions if the combined total exceeds the maximum permitted. The conditions are that:

- the roof height is not increased;
- the angle of a roof facing the public highway is not changed.

Porches. These are permitted up to the limits of:

- a floor area of three square metres;
- a height of three metres.

Gates, fences and walls. These are allowed up to one metre high when adjoining a road, or two metres high in other places.

There are other permitted developments, and if you require information about these or if there is any confusion over whether your particular development is allowable, you should contact the planning department and if necessary seek written verification that planning permission is not required. It is always advisable to check anyway, as the rules can, and do, change from time to time.

When planning permission is required
If your proposal does not come under the heading of 'permitted development', or if it involves 'change of use', you will have to make a planning application (approximate £30 fee). 'Change of use' is where, for example, you convert an existing house into flats. An initial chat with your planning officer will establish whether what you want to do is acceptable in principle (although it will be an opinion only) and may save you the cost of having detailed drawings produced if your proposed project is out of the question. In any case, he can advise on the method of application.

A general guide to the procedure is as follows:

- Submit the application form (and fee) along with detailed drawings of the proposed scheme (normally at 1:50 scale). Drawings would be floor plans, and also elevations (vertical plans) if the outside of the house or neighbouring properties are affected.

   Drawings would normally have to be done professionally, but you can do your own if you are able, especially if the project is fairly small and uncomplicated. The drawings should show details of

   - any structural alterations (eg the removal of a load-bearing wall and the method for subsequently supporting the structure – RSJs etc); and
   - details relating to plumbing, drainage, doors, windows, ventilation etc.

The more information that is available, the easier (and quicker) your application will be to process. You will need several (at least four) copies of the drawings, some of which the planning department will then issue to other departments, including

- the Building Inspector (also called the District Surveyor, Building Control Officer or Borough Surveyor). He is responsible for building operations associated with planning/building regulations;
- the Environmental Health Officer. He is responsible for work under grants, and sometimes other work;

- the Historic Buildings Office (if relevant).

All these departments are responsible for checking on the work as it is carried out.

Local authorities are usually easy to approach and discuss matters with, and will offer help if you need to make minor alterations to your project. A planning guide called *A House-holder's Guide to Planning Permission* is published by Planning Aid for Londoners (PAFL) and is available from their office (price £1.50) at 100 Minories, London EC3N 1JY.

The Department of the Environment (DOE) also publishes a brochure entitled 'Planning Permission: A Guide for House-holders', which is available free of charge from: The Department of the Environment, Distribution, Building 3, Victoria Road, Ruislip, Middlesex HA4 0NZ.

If you are employing a professional to run your project he will handle all the planning arrangements.

Trees
If your development involves drastic pruning or removal of any tree, you must check that there is not a preservation order in force, otherwise you could face a stiff fine. A recent case involved action by neighbours and a substantial fine against a developer who was thus forced to suffer a much-reduced profit on the sale of his property after removing a protected tree.

Building regulations

Whether or not planning permission is necessary for your project, you will have to comply with the building regulations. These are legal requirements and are the responsibility of the Building Inspector (or District Surveyor) and the Environmental Health Officer. Fees are payable for their services (see page 69).

If you have submitted detailed drawings of your project for planning approval these should have included anything that related to building regulations, and should go to the relevant departments automatically (although it is worth checking yourself).

If planning approval was not needed, and therefore drawings were not produced, you must still notify the departments concerned with building regulations and you do this by sending a *building notice.* You are not allowed to start your project until this notice has been received, and approval given. Once the job is running the work is then inspected at intervals to make sure that everything is in order.

As with planning applications the approval process can be lengthy, and you should therefore submit details of your project at an early stage. Building regulations cover various aspects of building work, including structure, fire regulations, ventilation, stairways, room heights, drainage, water supply etc, and it is an offence not to comply with them. Approval for building regulations is quite separate from planning approval.

If you are employing a professional he will make the necessary applications and arrangements for compliance with the regulations, and if you are not, you should contact the relevant departments of your local authority for information about how to prepare your own applicaion, and the procedure to adopt.

There are exemptions to the building regulations, for example:

- open-sided car ports not exceeding 30 square metres
- conservatories.

However, it is always wise to check if you are unsure.

HMSO publishes a guide called *Manual to the Building Regulations 1985*, which is available from HMSO, PO Box 15, 49 High Holborn, London WC1V 6HB.

Chapter 10
Getting the Work Done

This chapter deals with the way in which the client manages the jobs that are carried out on his home.

Small jobs and odd jobs

Some examples, and where to find people to do them, are listed in Chapter 2. The type of person you are looking for could be a local handyman, perhaps one who works at the weekends or in the evenings, especially for the really small jobs such as putting up bookshelves, repairing fences etc. This may not be an ideal arrangement for you, but you may not be in a position to choose. Getting people to do small jobs can be difficult, and it is worth taking the trouble to fit in with their work schedule, and being prompt about payment, as you may want to use them again, and perhaps on a regular basis.

Some pensioners will do small jobs and can often be very skilled and experienced. Youngsters are also worth considering, especially for heavy or gardening jobs, again maybe at evenings and weekends.

It is best to agree an hourly rate and pay in cash for jobs of this type. If materials are required you can either collect them yourself, or order them by telephone and quote your credit card number or pay cash on delivery. This will avoid paying sums of money in advance to people you do not know who may then disappear. It is fairly unlikely that people doing this type of work would be VAT registered, which will help to keep down the costs of small jobs.

Emergency work

This is the most urgent repair work that affects nearly everyone at some time or another, and the better you maintain your property and its fixtures and installations the less likely you are to need it. It is usually the most expensive type of work you can have done, when you take into account the cost of the time spent and the fact that you may have to have an emergency repair fixed again – this time more permanently. However, if you *do* need an emergency service, ask before you call them out exactly what their charges are (see page 62), and whether there will be any additional charges. Whatever the repair is, it will be done a lot more quickly (and cheaply) if it is made as easy as possible. For example, if there is a water leak in your loft, make sure that a ladder is available and that any stored items are moved out of the way. Also try to arrange some temporary lighting if none exists.

The gas board will, in an emergency, turn off your gas at the meter or in the road for the appropriate call-out fee (see page 62). You can avoid this fee by turning it off yourself if the meter is accessible and it is possible to do so without danger to anyone, although if the escape is on the pipework between the road and the meter you won't be able to turn it off yourself. It will then be up to you to have faulty pipework or equipment replaced or repaired at your convenience as urgent but non-emergency work.

The same applies with electricity. If there is a fault you can turn everything off at the consumer unit, again if it is safe to do so, rather than pay the call-out charge (page 62). The repair can then be carried out as non-emergency work. If the fault is on the 'live' side of the consumer unit you will *have* to call out the emergency service.

In the event of a water leak the water authority's emergency service will isolate the pipework at the nearest stopcock, or turn everything off at the main stopcock – again something you can do yourself if you know where the stopcocks are. To turn the water off outside your house (in the front garden or on the pavement), you will need a special key which can be obtained from your builders merchant or DIY shop. Again, once the supply is turned off there is no longer an emergency. An emergency plumber, on the other hand, may be able to make a repair on the spot, which will leave you with water but a hefty bill. You have to decide, comparing cost and convenience, whether to have a repair done in the middle of the night or (more cheaply) as soon as possible afterwards.

Don't forget that if there is a leak in your central heating system, the gas, the electric power point and the water main supplying it will all have to be turned off, and the system drained.

So, to avoid unnecessary emergency call-out charges, turn off the appropriate main supply yourself, if it is safe to do so, and have any repairs carried out during normal working hours.

House diary

In a well-ordered household the names and telephone numbers of emergency services and specialists will be readily to hand. For the rest there will be a desperate search through the Yellow Pages or the local paper, probably at a very inconvenient moment. One way to minimise the effects of a household emergency, and to help with general repair and maintenance work, is to equip yourself with a 'house diary'. This can contain such information as:

- day and night telephone numbers of gas, water and electricity emergency services;
- telephone numbers of electricians, plumbers, builders and other trade specialists;
- descriptions of the location of water stopcocks, gas cocks, electricity consumer units, cold water tanks, central heating feed tank and system drain-off point;
- details of the make, model and reference numbers of your central heating boiler and any associated equipment (useful if parts need to be ordered), and any other appliances.

You can make the list as comprehensive as you like, but just having basic information to hand will help enormously when the need arises.

Maintenance and repair work

Try not to leave maintenance and repair until something goes wrong or breaks down.

Maintenance is one of those subjects that a lot of people would like to forget about, or wonder why it hasn't been technologised out of existence. Nevertheless, those who religiously have their appliances serviced, their brickwork repointed (joints between bricks cleaned out and re-cemented), and their houses painted regularly are the ones who generally have fewer major repair bills.

One example of how lack of maintenance can cause major problems is where missing or broken roof slates or tiles are not attended to. Once water is allowed to penetrate it can damage roof timbers, plaster, ceilings, wiring and decoration, and can cause rot, fungal growth and cracks, all of which can be expensive to put right. So regular maintenance is important.

Even obvious maintenance jobs are sometimes forgotten about, with the inevitable consequences. For example, central heating radiator valves that drip slightly are ignored and left, sometimes for years, and all for the sake of a couple of hours of work. The results are normally ruined carpets, rotten floorboards and joists, damaged ceilings, and so on. A list of 'who does what' is given on page 12, and some of the contractors mentioned will carry out regular (contract) maintenance, especially for central heating and other installations.

Some examples of jobs which should be done regularly are:

- external painting – walls, windows, doors;
- inspection of roof – refix slates or tiles;
- brickwork repointing;
- repairs to cracked or broken steps;
- pruning trees (to limit the spread of roots near the house or drains);
- servicing, inspection and repair of all water, gas and electrical installations and appliances, drains, gutters and rainwater pipes;
- replacement of rotting timber (window frames etc).

Gas, electricity and water authorities

If your job involves any of the above services, you should obtain and accept estimates in advance of the job starting, but in consultation with your builder, as often there is a lengthy period between acceptance and start dates.

Leaving it all until the last minute may delay your job considerably. For example, the laying of a new water main might be necessary before foundations can be laid for a new rear extension.

You also have to comply with the regulations governing these services, which the relevant authority can advise upon.

Party walls

A party wall is a wall between one property and another where the properties are joined together (ie the wall is common to both properties). For a pair of semi-detached houses there is one party wall between the two. For terraced houses there are two party walls to each house, except for the 'end of terrace' houses, which will have one each.

If your property has one or more party walls and you intend to carry out building works, you should consider how your neighbour could be affected. Any structural work that is carried out could affect neighbouring properties, whether the work is directly connected with the wall or not. For example, knocking a hole through the *back* wall of your house (perhaps for new french windows) could cause cracks to appear in an adjoining property.

If you intend to carry out structural works, you will need to have a building surveyor to look at the proposed works in relation to neighbouring properties, and to advise about possible effects on those properties.

Walls between houses can be quite thin (9in, or double skins of brickwork) so even relatively minor work can affect your neighbours, eg hacking off plaster, drilling holes for shelves.

If you want to remove a chimney breast which forms part of a party wall, the wall can be weakened, with resulting damage to the ajoining property.

It is important, therefore, before starting *any* work which could affect the party wall, that you contact your neighbour and explain what you intend to do. Make an inspection of his property, noting any cracks, stains due to water penetration, bulges on the party wall itself and on adjacent walls. Also check for sticking doors and windows, as these can be an indication of existing subsidence, something you would need to know about before you started work, on large jobs, otherwise you could be accused of causing it as a result of the work you had carried out. Make a list of any such defects and ask your neighbour to acknowledge them, so that should there be any subsequent dispute about damage you will be able to show what existed prior to the work being started. Taking photographs of obvious defects can also be helpful.

You should also sort out the insurance situation before any work starts, as a subsequent claim against you for damage to your neighbour's property, especially where major work was involved, without an insurance policy in force, wouldn't bear thinking about. You, your contractor and your neighbour should all have policies relating to damage (see Chapter 8 on insurance).

Before actually starting any significant work on your property, ask your neighbour to remove pictures, mirrors and anything else breakable, from the party wall area, and block up fireplace openings to stop dust and soot going into his rooms via chimneys.

Party wall regulations for London are included in the London Building Acts. These regulations impose conditions for notification of proposed works to owners of adjoining properties. This is especially important if you live in a block of flats, where you could be 'adjoined' on several sides. If you fail to notify your neighbours, they may be able to prevent you from doing the work.

If you propose to build an extension to your property which involves the erection of a party wall and planning permission, the local authority will normally advise the owners of neighbouring properties, who have the right to object. Whether or not planning permission is required you will normally need the agreement of your neighbour to your proposal. This is known as a 'party wall agreement', and you can get advice on the subject from your local authority, a solicitor or a building surveyor, and you should do so well in advance of organising the work.

The Royal Institution of Chartered Surveyors publishes a guide – *Party Wall Legislation and Procedure* – which is available from: The RICS Bookshop, 12 Great George Street, London SW1P 3AD.

Medium to large jobs

Examples of these are listed on page 14, along with suggestions of where to find people to do them.

Although this chapter is concerned with employing contractors on your own, it should be said that in any case you would not normally use a professional to manage jobs such as having double glazing or central heating installed, but the exception might be where they were being installed as part of a total refurbishment of a property. As far as loft conversions and extensions are concerned, whether or not a professional is used would probably depend on the size and/or the complexity of the job, and your confidence in the ability of the builder.

Once estimates are accepted and planning and/or building regulation approval is obtained (if necessary) the job is ready to go ahead.

Preparations

With start dates agreed you need to make certain preparations. You will have to make arrangements for:

- money to cover initial payments or deposits to be available;
- access to your property (how contractors will get in and out);
- spare keys to be cut;
- storing valuables away in a safe place;
- advising immediate neighbours of impending noise and comings and goings;
- pets to be looked after;
- any temporary accommodation needed while your house is uninhabitable;
- carpets to be taken up or dust sheets to be available.

Arrange to be at home when contractors first arrive. Explain about means of access, keys and security, which toilets and washing facilities can be used. Designate areas for storage of materials and equipment. Ask whether main services (gas, water, electricity) will be cut off for any period. Make any initial payments that have been agreed in advance. If you are not going to be at home during the day, leave telephone numbers where you can be contacted. Ask about daily start and finish times and about how many people will be on site daily. If you are going to be living in the house throughout the work, explain that you would like it kept tidy, and show them where the vacuum cleaner is.

Living through the work

One of the hardest things for many people to come to terms with is the upheaval and mess caused by having building and other work done in the home. The disruption to a previously ordered household can test your sense of well-being and good nature to the point where you wish that you had left everything as it was. However, disruption is something that has to be put up with occasionally, otherwise your house would eventually collapse around you.

Others are more able to accept that the condition is, after all, only temporary, and some even enjoy seeing improvements taking place in their home, and get on well with the 'family' of contractors who have moved in. If you are not one of those, one way to prepare yourself is to try to imagine what your home will look like when the work is finished, rather than despairing of its condition while the work is going on.

There are things that you can do to help the situation. Try to move out of the work and 'traffic' areas if possible, although obviously kitchens and bathrooms will have to be used. It is quite common for people to abandon a large part of their house and live in bedrooms and even attics while the main rooms are being worked in, and this makes life much easier for contractors, and speeds up the job, because floors, carpets and furniture do not have to be replaced every night when work has finished. Sometimes arrangements can be made, sometimes they cannot.

Contractors would normally be expected to leave your home in a reasonable condition when the day's work has finished. They should clear up any mess that they have made, stack rubbish in bags or in a skip, and store materials tidily in mutually agreed areas. They should take up dust sheets and brush carpets. Stairs and hallways should be left unobstructed. Openings for new windows and doors should be temporarily sealed and made secure, and floors should be replaced in usable areas. This should leave you with perhaps some dusting and a trip round with the carpet sweeper, depending on how particular you are.

Make sure that you are left with some usable electrical power points, and at the very least – *cold* water. You may be without baths and heating for some periods.

There are occasions when you have to be prepared to rough it for a while, especially when several contractors are working at the same time, as it is extremely difficult to carry out major works in a house or flat without seriously inconveniencing the occupants.

Your attitude

Building/contracting operations hardly ever run completely smoothly. You can't expect all the work to be carried out from beginning to end without some hitches. Contractors are human too and each job they take on presents them with a unique set of problems, which all have to be overcome.

In order to give the contract a chance to work well, it is necessary for you to adopt certain attitudes in your dealings with the people working on your property. Being pedantic and overbearing, for example, is certain to create a chasm between you and them. Being too soft, and tacitly accepting both good and bad workmanship, unacceptable delays etc, won't create the right atmosphere either, and could lead to lack of respect for you, and the contractors feeling that they can do what they like. The happy medium, as always, is the answer. You should be businesslike but friendly, and understanding but conscious of the fact that you are the employer and they are the employed.

Working relationships

Good working relationships are essential to the successful day-to-day running of your job, and a set of conditions has to be established whereby you and your employees can operate together. Achieving this can make the difference between a happy, well-run job and a nightmare.

Relationships can thrive on small things like making tea and coffee facilities available, and having the occasional chat about what is being done, even if you don't understand the technicalities of it. Contractors will feel endeared to you if they think that their work is being appreciated, and most will respond in a positive way, making sure that the necessary effort is put into making the contract work well.

If the working relationship is bad the contractors will not enjoy working on your property and will just be waiting for the end of the job so that they can get away from it. This can have an adverse effect on workmanship and overall performance.

Site meetings and minutes

On a large, professionally organised job, site meetings can be fairly formal affairs arranged at fixed intervals. The people attending will be the professional (the client's representative), the quantity surveyor (if used), the main contractor and any combination of sub-contractors and other specialists – depending on the stage the job is at and who is involved at the time. The client will not normally attend these meetings. Whether the job is professionally run or not the purpose of the meetings is the same – to discuss progress, any delays to the job, any extra work or variations, any additional costs, late deliveries of materials, and any other problems. As different items are dealt with, the course of action is decided upon and the person responsible is notified. On smaller jobs, meetings can be on the basis of an informal discussion between you and your builder, although all the subjects mentioned above are still relevant and just as important.

During the course of these meetings various statements are made, and decisions taken, which should be recorded as having happened on that day at that meeting. This record is called the *minutes*. It would be to your advantage to keep the minutes of site meetings. This record will prove invaluable as a reference document at future meetings, and in the event of any dispute. The example on page 93 shows columns for 'matters arising', 'decision' and 'action', which should include the names of those concerned.

Size of the workforce

The builder, or the main contractor, decides how many people will work on the site at any one time, as he is responsible for organisation, working conditions and safety.

He will bring in his own employees as and when he needs them, and will tell sub-contractors and others when they are required on site, taking into account the fact that the contract should be finished by a certain date – not only for the client's benefit but also to ensure a reasonable profit for himself.

If there is a works programme (pages 90–91) showing when the various parts of the contract are to be carried out, the client can see at a glance who should be on site, although not necessarily the number of persons from each company.

The sub-contractors will come and go as their part of the contract is carried out, while the builder and his own employees should remain on the site for the duration of the contract. On a small contract the builder may, if there is insufficient work of his own to keep him there full time, visit the site at regular intervals to keep a check on who is there and the progress made.

If you are dissatisfied with progress, or the programme isn't being adhered to, the reason may be that there are insufficient people on the site. One or two people on a sizeable job is obviously not enough, and you would have to remind the builder of his obligations, being firm and businesslike, but not rude. It is just possible that there is a temporary lull in the operation because of an unforeseen hitch, which will be righted in a day or two.

It is a good idea for you to keep a daily record of the number of

Programme for a small site

	Weeks:	1	2	3	4	5	6	7	8	9	10	11	12	13	14	15	16	17	18	19
Scaffolding/preparation		▓																		
Structural brickwork			▓	▓																
Telephone				▓																
Fix steel work/new windows																				
Damp proof course					▓															
Remove old doors/plaster			▓																	
Roof work						▓														
Electricity and gas							▓													
Internal partitions/alterations								▓												
Wiring first fix								▓												
Lay solid floors/tiles							▓													
New manhole/drainage								▓												

	Internal doors/woodwork	Strengthen and repair front steps	External render/repairs	Internal plastering	External plumbing	Skirting and second fix woodwork	Central heating and internal plumbing	Kitchen and bathroom fitments	Wiring/electrical second fix	Painting internal/external	Garden/landscaping	Carpets/cleaning	Clear site

people on the site, and what they are doing there, so that you can refer to it should the contract overrun, or if there is a dispute of some kind later on.

Extra work

Whatever the job that you have been quoted for entails, it is often the case that something additional crops up, either as an unforeseen element of the job itself, or as another piece of work that you would like to have done at the same time. Whenever extra work is required, safeguard yourself by getting some idea of the cost before that work is started. Labour is expensive, and additional work that you considered incidental could be way out of proportion to the cost of the original job. If a contractor tells you that extra work is required, ask him to explain exactly what it is and why it wasn't included in the estimate. If your estimate was a complete 'labour and materials' price, eg £500 for the tiling of a bathroom, and the contractor had measured the area beforehand, he couldn't then expect you to pay more if he ran out of tiles. His error in measuring would be his fault. However, if part of the wall he was tiling was faulty and broke away – something that he couldn't have foreseen, or been expected to know about – the additional cost of making good the wall would have to be borne by you, as it was not included in the estimate.

One of the benefits of having a detailed estimate is that when the question of extra work comes up you can check the relevant item, and you then have some basis for any query about whether extra costs are involved.

If a large amount of extra work is needed and will be too costly for your budget (maybe a collapsed drain that was not discovered until work started), you may be faced with having to omit something else in order to pay for it. Perhaps there is something that is not essential, or that can be put off until a later date (such as the new patio).

Contingency sums

For medium to large jobs it is usual to leave a sum of money (between 5 and 10 per cent) in reserve to cover the cost of any unexpected additional work which could not have been known about at the time of estimating. For example, the discovery of dry or wet rot when floors were taken up.

By including this sum in your overall budget for the job, you ensure that certain additions or variations to the contract can be dealt with quickly, and will not cause delays, which might be the case if you had suddenly to find extra funds.

Minutes of site meeting at
'The Gables', 15 New Street, Anytown on 9 March 1990 at 10.30 am

Those present:	xxxxxxxxxx	Main contractor
	xxxxxxxxxx	Heating Sub-contractor
	xxxxxxxxxx	Electrical Sub-contractor
	xxxxxxxxxx	Roofing Sub-contractor

Matters arising	Decision	Action
yyyyyyyyyyyy	oooooooooo	JK
yyyyyyyyyyyy	ooooooooooo	BLC Ltd

Keeping an eye on the work

If all is going well on your job, you can keep a reasonably low profile, something that will be appreciated by the people you have working there, and you can confine yourself to general organisation. If all is not going well, you will have to become more involved.

Obvious things to look for when inspecting a job are progress, quality of workmanship, the number of contractors on site, any damage to the building and/or contents, and cleanliness and tidiness, especially if you are living in the property. Check also on whether materials and equipment are on the site when they should be.

If you make regular payments (stage payments) based on the amount of work completed by a certain date, make sure that the respective amount of work has in fact been carried out, and that materials being claimed for are actually there on the site and the value of them is correct.

If the builder, or main contractor, is supplying other trades, they will be sub-contractors to him, and he will pay them (albeit from the money you pay him), and they will be his responsibility. However, you should still inspect the work that they do, and report anything you are not satisfied with to the main contractor himself. You should not give direct instructions to his sub-contractors nor criticise their work directly.

If you have employed various contractors independently, you may well have several on your job at any one time. You will have to supervise each one separately, just as a main contractor would do if he was employing them, to monitor progress and standards of workmanship and to make sure that overpayments are not made. If a particular contractor says that he has finished, you should inspect his work thoroughly and make sure that there are no forgotten or outstanding items.

In the case of installations, eg kitchens, central heating etc, you need to ask the contractor for an explanation and a demonstration of how they work once the work is finished. Check at this stage that everything *does* work and that you understand any controls.

The most difficult part of many jobs is the finish. Any problems or misunderstandings that have occurred throughout the contract are brought to a head when the final assessment comes and the final payment is imminent.

The contractors are ready to leave to start other jobs, and the client is aware that all the odds and ends must be sorted out, otherwise it will mean getting contractors to come back. Always try to avoid the situation where little bits are left, because nobody really wants to have to return to a job for an hour or two.

If things are not to your liking, do not make the final payment until the agreed and estimated work is complete to a reasonable standard. If there are outstanding items that really cannot be finished, for whatever reason, an appropriate amount should be deducted from the final payment to cover them. The contractor(s) should readily agree to a deduction of this nature and, as far as the client is concerned, keeping some money in hand means that the relevant contractor will return reasonably promptly when the work is ready for completion.

Inspection of work before final payment

The most important aspect of the job for you is the finished product. It is what all the effort, time and money has been aimed at, and is what you will have to live with. So it is worth doing a thorough check of everything before accepting the work. Read through your estimates, specifications, contracts etc, and note any alterations, deletions or variations.

The larger the job, the longer this will take and the more important it will be, but it must be done at this stage. When contractors have gone you won't want to see them again, even if you got along very well with them. You will want your house back and you won't want to trip over a bag of cement or a ladder for a long time to come.

So with your estimates in your hand, walk around the job, preferably when contractors are not there and it is quiet, and start to check everything. Make a list of everything that isn't as it should be. On a major refurbishment, loft conversion or extension to the property there will be many individual things to check so it will be easier if you break them down into headings, eg carpentry, electrical work etc. Examples of what to look for are:

- New walls and ceilings – cracks; shrinkage; unevenness; damp patches.
- Decoration – poor paint finish (rough to touch or discoloured); peeling wallpaper, wrong type of paint used (emulsion instead of gloss); runs and bubbles in paintwork.
- Floors – protruding nails, loose, split or broken boards; loose or broken tiles; damaged, torn or burnt carpets.
- Roofs – missing or broken slates or tiles; flashing not intact or badly fitted; gutters and rainwater pipes in place and not leaking. You can test the roof and the gutters/pipes by playing a hose on the roof (as long as you can reach it safely).
- Plumbing – that hot and cold taps work, and the water pressure is reasonable; that toilets flush properly; that baths and basins don't leak; that tanks are not leaking, and are insulated; that pipework in exposed areas is insulated; that all sanitary ware is securely fixed.
- Central heating – that all radiators get hot; that all valves turn on and off; that all controls work; that the hot water cylinder

heats up; that there are no fumes from the boiler, or any gas leaks.

- Electrical – lights and power points that don't work; loose fittings; unclipped or unprotected cables; that circuit breakers and any new appliances work.
- Other – that all latches, catches, handles etc are fitted and work; that all doors, drawers and windows open fully, and don't stick; that loft hatches are fitted.

Don't forget to check major items such as whether walls are vertical and true, and ceilings are level and straight.

The list can go on but the message is obvious – check everything carefully. As mentioned before, don't expect a top-class job from a cheap estimate. As long as you get what you pay for, and the work is to a reasonable standard, that should be satisfactory.

Any items which require attention should be listed and presented to the contractor. This list is known as a *snagging list*.

Having work inspected

When a professional has been employed to manage a contract he should inspect all the work as a matter of course, and will not issue a completion certificate until everything is satisfactory.

If you have hired builders/contractors yourself there are several ways of having work inspected, should the need arise. They are:

- friends who are architects/surveyors/builders etc;
- organisations with codes of practice relating to safety, eg CORGI and NICEIC (see pages 132–135). They will inspect their members' work;
- water authorities – they will ensure that installations conform to their standards and rules (new rules are currently being introduced – 1989);
- gas boards – they will inspect gas pipework and appliances for gas soundness, and compliance with legal requirements;
- electricity boards – they will inspect installations (eg the rewiring of a house) and appliances for safety and current practice requirements.

The charges for inspection by the different boards vary from area to area, but are in the range of £15 to £35 plus VAT for an initial period, followed by their respective time charges.

The local authorities (planning and building inspectors) have to inspect any work with which they have been involved, and you or your builder should notify them when that work is ready. Their inspection is important because if the work doesn't comply with the regulations you may have to have it altered or replaced.

Defects liability period

This usually relates to where a JCT or other form of written contract has been used (see page 52), but it can be operated for building projects organised and run by the client.

If it is to be instituted it has to be agreed in advance. You cannot suddenly tell your builder at the end of the job that you are holding back a percentage of his final payment as a retention sum. A builder might not be so keen to agree to a defects liability period without a JCT contract being used, as he would not have the benefit of a third party (the professional) to inspect the work.

He could become involved in all sorts of problems if the client, with little or no knowledge of building work, attempted to produce a schedule of defects.

Black economy/moonlighting

The term 'black economy' relates to payment in cash to contractors and others where the intention is not to declare the income to the Inland Revenue or Customs and Excise (for VAT). The advantage to the client is a cheaper job (he hopes) although, because there is normally nothing in writing, any claim in the event of a dispute could be difficult and embarrassing. The advantage to the contractor is that he pays no income tax or VAT if he doesn't register the payments in his accounts. It is, of course, illegal to evade income tax and VAT.

'Moonlighting' is doing jobs at evenings and/or weekends in addition to a regular daytime job.

Chapter 11

If Things Go Wrong

Whenever contractors are employed problems and hitches of all kinds can arise. Most are minor and are easily sorted out. Sometimes, however, whether you are using a professional or not, disagreements occur which take hold and become disputes, and the bigger they become the harder they are to resolve.

Whatever the severity of the problem it is always better to sort it out 'on site' rather than become involved in any formal proceedings, such as arbitration or even legal action. It is worth keeping in mind that all you really want is your job finished to the agreed standard, not a protracted battle resulting in delays and possible extra expense. Disputes can arise whatever the size of the job, but the larger jobs are usually those that present the most complications.

The golden rule whenever anything goes wrong is – keep calm. Discuss the problem logically and try to find ways round it. It will be to both yours and your contractor's advantage. Also, try to sort out difficulties as they occur. Leaving them until the end of the job is bound to result in a dispute about final payment.

Damage to property

It is always wise, when work is going on in the home, to store away articles of real or sentimental value, and anything breakable. However careful everyone may be, though, things still get damaged, especially carpets, paintwork, decorations, and (further up the scale) ceilings, doors, windows and sometimes the fabric of the building itself.

When accepting contractors' estimates you should have checked that the contractors were insured in respect of your property. You should also have made sure that your own insurance was sufficient and up to date. However, it is not always worth claiming on insurance policies for very small amounts. If someone working in your home breaks or damages something it can be easier for him to replace it, or deduct the value from the bill.

Where damage amounts to a more sizeable sum, eg where your builder puts his foot through the ceiling and a section has to be replaced, it may still be easier for him just to go ahead and do it, especially if men and materials are on site, rather than become involved with claim forms, loss adjustors etc. A satisfactory job is all that is required.

If the damage is such that an insurance claim *has* to be made, make sure that everything is listed and itemised and that it all goes on the claim form. Consult your own insurance company for advice, as insurance of some works is the responsibility of the employer (you), and other works that of the contractor.

In the event of major and/or structural damage you will need a proper survey (by a qualified surveyor) to ascertain the full extent of the damage – perhaps to include adjacent buildings, because your neighbour could have a claim against you for damage to his property.

If a contractor you employed (maybe for a small job) causes damage and has no insurance, he may be willing to carry out the necessary repairs at his own expense. If he is not willing you may have to consider taking legal advice, depending upon the extent of the damage and/or whether you are able to claim on your own policy.

If a professional has been employed to manage your job he can assist in the claims process, and if a JCT form of contract has been used, the insurance requirements will have been detailed in the contract form.

To sum up:

- minor damage – settle there and then without an insurance claim, if possible;
- expensive (non-structural) damage – make an insurance claim;
- major damage involving structure – always seek professional advice and have a structural survey carried out. Your own insurance company will advise about the claims procedure.

Lack of continuity

Your job should progress at a reasonable rate and you have a legal right to expect it to be finished within a reasonable time. Your contract may have specified start and finish dates, which the contractor is bound to adhere to (barring certain unforeseen problems or additional work). When a works programme is drawn up (see pages 90–91) it is normally based on continuity of work, ie one job follows on from the last and some overlap, so that the site is continually manned, although some contracts are deliberately separated into phases with gaps in between – possibly to suit the client's accommodation or financial requirements.

It is normal to expect people to be working on your job every day and you should make a point of checking on who is there. If the site is unmanned for any period, or there are insufficient numbers of people working there, you should communicate with your contractor as soon as possible and ask him for the reason for the delay. Politely remind him that you expect your job to continue at a reasonable pace. Excuses made by him about his sub-contractors not being available are not acceptable. He should have had plenty of time to organise them, and they are his responsibility. There can, of course, be valid reasons for lack of continuity, eg adverse weather conditions.

If a professional is running your job he will investigate delays, assess whether they are acceptable and take any necessary action.

Disputes with contractors

This section relates to where the client employs contractors on his own (where an architect or surveyor is not used to run the job), although there are some references to professionals. Where a professional *is* used to run a job, any problems that arise under the terms of the contract would be handled by him, and he would also act as your adviser in the event of a dispute.

Most disputes between client and contractor are about payment, delays, quality of workmanship and/or materials or extra work. Minor disputes can normally be resolved by discussion and in specific cases by reference to your estimate and/or contract (one good reason for having everything in writing).

Major disputes are difficult to handle as there could be legal implications; for example, where the builder removes all his men from the site, or you delay payment to the builder. It is always better to try to resolve disputes by negotiation rather than resorting to arbitration procedures or even legal action. To begin with, as soon as you start any proceedings your job will probably stop completely. There will be the inevitable lengthy saga of solicitors, inspections of the work etc, and finally you will probably have to find another builder to finish the job. Problems aren't always the contractor's fault, of course. There are two parties to the contract and your contractor could have a claim against you for delays to the contract caused by your unreasonable behaviour. For example:

- denying full and proper access to the site
- obstructing the men on the site
- asking the men to leave the site.

Using a professional. Disputes between architect and contractor, while not directly involving the client, could affect the running of the job. However, it would be unwise of the client to interfere in any such dispute.

Poor workmanship/materials

All workmanship and materials should be to a basic satisfactory standard, based on what is normally and generally accepted. Anything not up to scratch should be pointed out to your contractor and then either removed and reinstated or altered, at no extra cost to you. You have to make regular inspections of the work to make sure that basic standards are being applied.

High standards can be obtained by using best quality materials and top quality specialist contractors, but of course the job will cost much more. You will have to be your own judge of what is acceptable and satisfactory, and examples of things to look for are:

- obvious damage to new work;
- uneven, lumpy or cracked plaster work to walls and ceilings;
- kitchen or bathroom units/cupboards not level or insecurely fixed;
- badly fitting new doors and windows;
- central heating radiators loose or not level;
- installation of non-specified equipment (eg wrong types of door).

Obviously, the more practically minded you are the easier it will be for you to examine the work being undertaken in your home. If you are completely non-practical, either leave everything to the contractor, if he seems reliable and experienced (and a lot of people do) or get the whole job checked when it is finished, and before you settle the bill. Tell your contractor before he starts the job if you intend to do this, and why, otherwise he may take exception to having his payment withheld while a stranger inspects his work. Also, telling him in advance might ensure that you get a better standard of workmanship.

If it comes to light, during an inspection, that workmanship is badly sub-standard, you have the right to ask the contractor to re-do the work to a reasonable standard (see Supply of Goods and Services Act). Likewise, if materials are not suitable for the purpose for which they have been used, you can ask the contractor to replace them.

The difference between suitability and quality should be understood. For example:

Suitability (or unsuitability) – a painter uses internal emulsion paint on the outside walls of your house.

Quality – a painter uses cheap quality external paint instead of best quality external paint on the outside walls of your house.

In the first instance there is absolutely no doubt that the wrong material has been used, and the job will have to be done again before payment can be made.

The implications of the second instance are not so clear cut. If you asked to have the outside of your house painted but did not specify a particular grade of paint, the painter could argue that his price for the job was based on the cheaper paint, and that if you had wanted the best paint you should have said so, and the price would therefore have been higher. If there was no discussion about which grade of paint was to be used, the issue could then be that the painter should have explained that there were different grades of paint, and given you the option of choosing and the cost involved.

Whatever the outcome of such a situation, it highlights the fact that you should always specify what you want done and which materials are to be used, and put it in writing. Discuss alternatives with your contractor and check on suitability of materials with manufacturers or builders merchants. It could be too late afterwards.

The control you have over the quality of your job hinges on the fact that you hold the purse strings, so before making payments make sure that you have:

- a reasonable standard of workmanship
- the agreed and specified materials.

If your contractor doesn't stick to either or both he has broken his contract with you, and if he refuses to rectify matters you should withhold payment and seek advice.

Using a professional. One of the duties of a professional during his inspections of the work is to keep an eye on standards of workmanship and on whether specified materials have been used. Anything not complying with the specification would be pointed out to the contractor. If you see something that is not to your liking, or appears to be wrong, point it out to your professional. You should always deal directly with your professional in a case like this, never the contractor, otherwise you could be seen as interfering with the running of the job.

Don't forget that your financial limits had a bearing on the quality of the contractor used and the materials specified. Your professional can only check that the specification is adhered to – not more.

Advice on handling disputes

When handling major disputes yourself the first step is to get some advice. Depending on what the dispute is about, some of the sources available to you are:

- your local Citizens' Advice Bureau;
- your local authority Trading Standards Officer;
- consumer organisations;
- community law centres;
- friends who are architects, surveyors, builders, solicitors etc (although it is generally unwise to involve friends in disputes);
- gas/electricity/water authorities – if the dispute involves their services;

- local authorities – if the dispute involves planning and/or building regulations;
- trades organisations and federations. If your contractor was a member of one of these organisations and was operating under a guarantee scheme they should be advised straight away of any dispute. Some organisations have conciliation/arbitration services and offer compensation if their members default. Details are on page 131.

The advice that you get may enable you to resolve the dispute, but if not you could, if your contractor agrees, use an arbitration service such as that operated by the Chartered Institute of Arbitrators (see page 130). Otherwise you may need to consult a solicitor. Try to find one who is familiar with building disputes, as it is a specialised field.

Using a professional. Where a professional has been employed to run your job he will be able to advise about matters relating to disputes with contractors. If a dispute becomes serious (for example, negotiations have broken down and your contractor has left the site), you can ask your professional to become involved in the process of taking action against the contractor, but you will have to pay for his time and it could be expensive.

Where a JCT MW 80 contract is in force its conditions provide for the referral of disputes to arbitration. If you agree to arbitration an arbitrator is appointed who looks at both sides of the dispute and makes a decision that must be accepted. Subsequent legal action in the courts cannot then be taken.

Liquidated damages

A clause may be included in your written contract for liquidated damages. Typically it would read 'liquidated damages of £300 per week'. This means that if the contract overruns or is abandoned by the contractor, the contractor has to pay the designated sum to the client, or have it deducted from payments made to him by the client for work that has been carried out. The money is intended to cover the client's losses if, for example, he is unable to occupy his property on the agreed finishing date and has to rent alternative accommodation – or if he is losing income (rent from the property because tenants are unable to occupy it).

Termination agreements

Some written contracts (although not the JCT) can contain a clause which states that a contract may be terminated (determined) by either party subject to the agreed notice being given. The period of notice would be stated in the contract. If no such clause exists, the contract can still be terminated if both parties agree.

You may wish to terminate a contract as a less harrowing alternative to legal action. As long as the financial situation is clear and satisfactory to both parties, it may be the best option in some cases of dispute, for example:

- unacceptable delay in starting your contract
- incompetence by the contractor.

There may also be the problem of default by the client (you). You may have trouble securing finance after the job has started (perhaps an expected loan was turned down), in which case the job would have to be stopped completely, or at a certain stage, and the contract terminated.

This may involve the contractor in a certain amount of expense (eg for materials and plant) and could upset his work schedule, leaving him with employees to pay and no other job ready for him to start. In a case like this he would normally have a claim against you for breach of contract. However, a mutual agreement to terminate the contract, with payment to the contractor for work completed, and an additional agreed payment to cover his expenses, loss of earnings etc, would be much better for both parties concerned than legal proceedings.

Termination of contracts

It is to be hoped that all your contracts will be concluded successfully, ie completed properly and within reasonable time to the satisfaction of all concerned. If that is the case you will have found responsible, reliable contractors whom you would use again and recommend to others.

If your job is not going well because of what you consider to be poor performance or unacceptable delay, it is important to establish what has caused the situation, and to attempt negotiation or perhaps arbitration before getting involved in terminating the contract. Delays, for example, could have been caused by any number of factors beyond the control of your contractor, for example:

- decisions regarding building regulations;
- hold-ups caused by work not carried out by gas/electricity/ water authorities;
- late information (from various sources including the client);
- inclement weather.

During the contract major problems might have been encountered with your property (subsidence, dry rot etc) which, being outside the scope of the original contract, could affect completion within the agreed time, either because the problems caused additional work or because their presence specifically delayed completion. While on the subject it should be mentioned that, whenever additional work is carried out during a contract, extra time must be allowed for that work – you can't pile weeks of extra work on your builder and still expect him to keep to his original completion date.

If you wish to terminate any contract you would be advised to take legal advice first. There have to be definite grounds for complaint by you. The fact that you don't like your builder is not a good enough reason to try to cancel his contract. The following are reasonable grounds for complaint:

- failure to keep to an agreed schedule
- failure to complete the contract on time
- failure to rectify earlier mistakes
- failure to use specified equipment and materials, and refusal to rectify
- disappearance from the site for unreasonable lengths of time
- abandonment of the contract
- bankruptcy.

The correct procedure must be adopted when terminating a contract, otherwise there could be problems if legal proceedings are subsequently instituted. The procedure to adopt is:

- Arrange a meeting with your contractor. It will be sensible for you to have a list of your complaints to hand and a witness to verify what is said. Take notes. Tell the contractor that you are not satisfied with his efforts so far. Ask what action he intends to take, and when. (If he agrees to put everything right, even though completion could be delayed, it might be more favourable to you than finding another contractor, additional expense etc.)

- Keep a record of the dates and times of all meetings.
- Write to the contractor listing your complaints and the dates of meetings. State the action you require him to take and the period he has to carry out the work. The period would depend on the condition of your job. If your roof had been worked on and left open to the elements, for example, you would need it put right quickly, say within 48 hours (otherwise you would be able to get it repaired by someone else and charge the cost to the first contractor). For other work you could give him 14 days, say, otherwise you will terminate his contract and employ another contractor. State that he will be charged for additional costs incurred by employing a second contractor. Send the letter by recorded delivery.
- If there is no response from the contractor in the time specified, write to him again stating that he is now in breach of contract and that you intend to go ahead and employ someone else to finish the work. Make clear that you intend to pay him only for the work he has done – not the full contract sum. State in the letter that he should now collect any equipment he has left on the site. Send this letter by recorded delivery also.
- You can issue a 'notice of default' which means that you are not obliged to pay any money to the first contractor until completion of the contract.
- In the case of bankruptcy or death of the contractor you should take specific legal advice, as the procedure becomes more complicated.

Using a professional. Problems with contractors would be the concern of a professional employed to manage your job, unless some of the contractors were employed directly by you. Some specialist firms prefer to have a contract directly with the client, rather than be sub-contractors even though an architect and main contractor are running the rest of the job. The reason is that they then avoid complicated written contracts, damages clauses and inspection by the professional, and can stipulate their own terms of payment, rather than wait for valuations to the main contract *and* be subject to retention sums. It is not always an ideal arrangement for the architect and the main contractor, as they have only limited control over that section of the work, and this can affect the overall running of the whole job. However, some firms will only work to their own terms and conditions – so if you want to use them that's the way it has to be. Termination of such contracts, should the need arise, would be between you and the firm concerned as your professional would not be involved.

Your professional will advise on the termination of a contract with which he has been involved and grounds for termination under the JCT MW 80 form of contract include:

- total suspension of the work by the contractor
- failure by the contractor to proceed regularly
- insolvency of the contractor.

Termination by the contractor
If your contractor notifies you that he intends to terminate the contract because of your actions or because there is a dispute over payment, you should get advice from your solicitor. If a professional has been used he will, of course, advise you.

Employing a second contractor

If all contact with the first contractor has ceased and you have informed him of your intentions, using the proper legal procedure, you will then be faced with the prospect of employing a second contractor to finish the job.

In order to protect yourself from any possible action by the first contractor, the second contractor must only carry out work that was specified in the original contract.

When selecting a second contractor you must use a company of similar size to the first one. It is no good employing a large organisation to finish a job started by a one-man band, the reason being that the price difference would be too great and a subsequent claim against the first contractor would be unreasonably high. You should also obtain two or three estimates to show that the contractor you have chosen is not wildly expensive.

You must tell the second contractor that he is being employed to finish a job started and abandoned by someone else, although he will probably realise that anyway. It has to be said that not every contractor likes to finish a job that has been started by someone else, or would wish to become involved in a job that is subject to an existing dispute. Some contractors may insist on taking out and re-doing all or part of the original work, on the basis that it is substandard, dangerous, or will adversely affect any work subsequently carried out by them. The estimate by the second contractor, therefore, could be even higher than the first. It is therefore advisable to have a proper survey of the original work carried out and a written report obtained, as an eventual claim against the first contractor by you for the difference between the two estimates may result in the first contractor insisting that his work was satisfactory. Try to agree the valuation of the original work with the first contractor.

A claim against the first contractor would be based on the following calculation:

	£
First contractor's estimate	15,800
Estimated value of first contractor's work	7,200
Difference	8,600
Cost of second contractor's work	9,800
Claim against first contractor	1,200

A legal point
Certain installations (eg a central heating system) are deemed to be fixtures in your property, and once installed cannot be removed in the event of a dispute, even if the installer has not been paid. He can, however, sue the person who employed him (you or the main contractor).

Disputes with professionals

The range of professionals who can be involved in your contract include an architect, a surveyor and a structural engineer. The professional bodies which govern their members' activities and specify codes of conduct are listed in Appendix 2.

If you feel that you are being badly represented by your professional, or your contract is not running as smoothly as you would like, for any number of reasons, the first thing to do is to have a meeting with him and discuss your grievances in a calm, business-like way. Establish that your dissatisfaction is connected with something that the professional himself has mishandled, or is responsible for. For example, he may be affected by delays relating to planning or building regulations – trying to get quick decisions from local authorities isn't always easy.

A meeting with your professional is important in that it should clear up any confusion. The professional has a difficult role in that he co-ordinates the whole contract, and he is in the front line when the client dishes out blame for delays, cost increases etc. Nevertheless, if you are still unhappy with the way your affairs are being managed and the dispute cannot be resolved, you can:

* contact a more senior member of the firm he works for;
* contact the secretary of the professional body to which he belongs and obtain a copy of the code of conduct. You may find that some codes only cover serious malpractice such as fraud or dishonesty, but exclude incompetence;
* use the arbitration service, if it exists, to try to resolve the dispute. Arbitration does not incur awards for legal costs;
* contact a solicitor with a view to legal action. Most professionals insure themselves against claims by clients and any award made to you would probably come from an insurance company, although if you lose you will be liable for the insurance company's legal costs;
* terminate the contract by mutual agreement, after settling payment for services to date.

Disputes with public services

As gas, electricity and water services are monopolies you do not have any choice about using them. This is a disadvantage to the consumer in the event of a dispute as the only really decisive action you can take, ie to stop using the service, is not an option that is normally available to you. Legal proceedings against them could be time-consuming, expensive and probably not worthwhile, except in the most serious cases, ie explosion or death.

Privatisation moves are currently (1989) under way for water and electricity authorities and this will mean the abolition of existing consumer consultative councils, and the setting up of customer service committees for each water company, and likewise for each region operated by the new electricity companies.

British Gas already has regional gas consumer councils and a national headquarters.

Addresses and telephone numbers can be obtained from your telephone directory.

Disputes with local authorities

These can arise over such matters as the refusal of a planning application, perhaps for an extension you want built. If your project is being handled by a professional, he will be able to deal with local authority requirements and any problems associated with them, although if a dispute occurs it may involve extra work for him, for which he will have to be paid. Your professional will advise you on the likely outcome of challenging a planning refusal, and will also advise you of the possible costs involved.

If you are dealing with the local authority yourself on the same issue, the first step before your planning application is refused is to go and discuss your proposal with the planning officer. It may be that a slight alteration to your scheme is all that is required in order to obtain the necessary approval.

If planning permission is rejected the planning department will give reasons for the refusal. If you believe the reasons to be unjust, or the result of maladministration, you can contact a councillor, whose name and address are available at the council office or at the Citizens' Advice Bureau.

Failing that, you can refer your case to the Secretary of State for the Environment to appeal against the decision.

Appeals against planning permission refusal

Once a decision by your local authority to refuse planning permission is made you have six months in which to make an appeal.

Before starting on this course of action it is worthwhile having an assessment of your particular case by a professional. If you did not use one to run your job you can hire one on a daily or hourly basis. Although this may sound like an expensive exercise, the advice you obtain will help you to decide whether or not it is worth going ahead with what could be an expensive and drawn-out process.

Appeals are made to the Secretary of State for the Environment, and the success rate is approximately 37 per cent (the national average for all types of appeal).

The Secretary of State can overturn a planning decision made by a local authority, and his decision will be based on a recommendation made by an inspector (who also has the power to take the decision).

The Department of the Environment issues a free guide to planning appeals which can be obtained from: The Planning Inspectorate, Department of the Environment, Tollgate House, Houlton Street, Bristol BS2 9DJ.

If your appeal is successful and planning permission is therefore granted, your local authority can, if it objects to the decision to overrule its refusal, in turn appeal to the High Court.

The Ombudsman service

Although not used very often, this service can be useful in extreme cases. There are different types of Ombudsman, but the one that concerns us here is the *Local* Ombudsman.

He will investigate complaints of maladministration by a local council or water authority. For example:

- neglect and unjustified delay
- failure to follow agreed policies, rules or procedure
- failure to have proper procedures
- malice, bias or unfair discrimination
- failure to provide advice or information when reasonably requested
- providing inaccurate or misleading advice
- failure to tell people of their rights.

There must be an injustice involved, not just a refusal – for example, on planning grounds. He does not have the power to overturn planning decisions either, but can *recommend* that a decision is changed or that compensation be paid.

Council activities which the Local Ombudsman can investigate include:

- planning
- building control
- drainage

- environmental health.

There are Local Ombudsmen for England, Scotland and Wales, and booklets and information can be obtained from your local council or Citizens' Advice Bureau, or from:

England
Local Ombudsman
21 Queen Anne's Gate
London SW1H 9BU

Local Ombudsman
29 Castlegate
York YO1 1RN

Scotland
Local Ombudsman
5 Shandwick Place
Edinburgh EH2 4RG

Wales
Local Ombudsman
Derwen House, Court Road
Bridgend
Mid-Glamorgan CF31 1BN

Liquidation

Liquidation is the winding-up of a limited company.

As far as a client is concerned, if a company carrying out his contract goes into liquidation, all work will cease and the men working on the job will leave.

There may be very little warning, or perhaps none at all, that a company is about to cease trading. It is often in the interests of the company not to broadcast the impending event.

A client can take some precautions against the possibility of a company that he employs going into liquidation. These include:

- making sure that payments made to any company he uses relate only to work actually completed or materials on the site (and sometimes off-site);

113

- employing a company under one of the warranty or guarantee schemes, such as those operated by the Federation of Master Builders, or the Building Employers Confederation (page 131), which will ensure that another contractor finishes the job in the event of default or insolvency.

Once a company goes into liquidation a liquidator is appointed to handle its affairs, call a meeting of the creditors and distribute the assets of the company. If you have a claim against the company you would be one of the creditors. Taking the company to court after it has gone into liquidation is difficult, although you can sometimes sue individual directors, for which you would need to take legal advice.

If the company has left materials on your job, you should take legal advice regarding ownership, although if you have paid for them they should be yours. Some sub-contractors to the company may have a claim to *their* materials if *they* have not been paid.

Being ripped off

This term normally applies to instances where clients are over-charged for goods or services, either because they are completely in the dark about what things should cost or are tricked, intimidated, talked into having something they do not need, or otherwise taken advantage of by a supplier or contractor.

Quite often a client is unaware that a rip-off has taken place until a long time after the event, and sometimes never.

What should you look out for?

People are tempted into paying cash for all kinds of jobs on their properties, generally because they think that they will save money and that the contractor will give them a discount. Sometimes you can save, but there are various ways of being caught as well. For example:

- handing over sums of money before the work has started or there are materials on the site. The contractor then disappears.
- being told that you will save VAT. Some contractors are not registered so you would not pay it anyway. (VAT is always charged on materials bought from a shop, but only on labour when the contractor is registered.)

- being told that the sum charged is high because it includes VAT, when the contractor is not registered and not legally allowed to charge VAT.
- no guarantees – if equipment breaks down or malfunctions you may not be able to get the installer to rectify it.
- no record of payments made – if confusion arises, the dishonest contractor can insist that he has received less than you actually paid him. Without a record there is no way of proving who is right, particularly where a series of payments is made over a period of time. (Always keep a record of money transactions, and get signatures for payments made.) You are particularly vulnerable when payments are made in cash because there are generally no written estimates or invoices, which means that checking on details is difficult.

Payment by cheque, although safer in many respects, does not prevent you from being taken advantage of. For example:

- not having a proper detailed estimate or contract means that, after the job has started, the contractor can say that certain items or parts of the work were not allowed for and are therefore extras requiring additional payment.
- you accept an estimate thinking that it includes everything. After the job has started and some payment has been made, the contractor informs you that the estimate was for his labour only and that he needs money for materials. Without a detailed estimate to refer to, you are faced with sacking the contractor and losing what you have already paid, or allowing him to continue with the freedom to charge you an unspecified amount for materials. Monitoring the materials used, especially on a large job, is difficult for the client, even if he has some practical knowledge. Of course, the clever (dishonest) contractor has stage-managed the whole affair, deliberately not being specific about whether labour and materials were both included, and waiting until the job had started and he had received some money before informing the client about the additional payment. (*Always* get detailed estimates.)
- the contractor charges the client for specialist skilled personnel and uses unskilled (cheap) labour.
- the contractor submits an extortionate estimate to the client for necessary sub-contract works, and does a private deal with the

sub-contractor for an agreed share-out of the excess amount.
● payment as the job progresses, without a clear idea of the extent of the work or proper supervision. In other words, allowing the contractor to start a job and agreeing to pay him a wage for each man he needs to employ (as and when necessary) plus any materials. On a reasonably large job the dishonest contractor is able to overcharge the unwary customer in a number of ways, such as:

- excessive amounts for materials
- materials not used
- hire equipment charged for but not used
- charging the client for more men than there are actually on the site, or for full days when parts of the day have been worked elsewhere. (If the client is out at work all day supervision is a problem.)
- paying the men on the site *substantially less* than the amount quoted and agreed with the client, with the contractor pocketing the difference. (A contractor would expect to make a *small* profit on the wages he paid to his men.)

Problems such as these normally arise where there is no professional supervision of the work and, of course, where the contractor is being deliberately dishonest. The examples show what can, and does, happen. The majority of people, however do not experience the direst of these, and contractors can be as honest as anybody else. If you think that you are being defrauded in any way you should seek professional help (contact an architect or a surveyor) for advice to assess whether what you are paying relates to the work you are having done. You may at least stop any further excessive payments.

Things you do not really need
Talking people into having various types of work or installation done in the home is the art of the salesman, and sometimes the contractor himself. Whether or not the work is necessary, or even desirable, is by the way. The point is that you can be convinced of the need for it. Various unethical ploys can be used to ensure that the customer signs a contract – 'for safety reasons', 'energy conservation', 'will add thousands to the value of your home' are just some of them. Some could even be true, but you should not

enter into a contract without a proper unbiased assessment of your needs, and before obtaining other estimates.

A cooling-off period now exists for contracts signed under certain conditions (see below). Contracts obtained using high-pressure sales techniques are often vastly overpriced and offer fat commissions for the salesmen concerned. One householder was so drained by hours of relentless pressure to sign a contract for a new kitchen that she eventually gave the salesman £50 just to get rid of him.

Give yourself time to think about the work before signing anything, and get advice and at least three estimates. Don't just accept the first one because you have 'made contact', and because it will save you 'shopping around'.

Cancellation rights

If you sign a contract to have work done in your home through someone who calls at your door without an appointment or through an unsolicited telephone call, you are allowed seven days to cancel the contract and ask for the return of any money that you have paid. This applies to home improvements (eg double glazing) but not to new building work (eg an extension to your house) for any amount over £35.

If you sign a contract at a company's business premises or if you pay in advance you do not have the right to cancel the contract. If you use a credit agreement and sign it at your home, you will receive a second copy of the contract or a second notice of your cancellation rights by post, and you then have a five-day 'cooling-off' period in which you can cancel the contract.

One couple's story

This story is true.

A and K bought a house in London. It was in no condition to live in so they contacted an architect to design a complete refurbishment. The architect was also to manage the job to completion.

A specification and drawings were produced and a formal JCT contract was drawn up with a builder of the clients' choice. They had seen his work elsewhere and were satisfied that he was the man they wanted. The job was started, with the builder and his employees on site. The clients lived in one room on the top floor. The only toilet was in the basement and was used by everyone. It was obviously difficult for the couple, but they put up with it because they had nowhere else to live.

After a while certain problems arose. The builder was installing fixtures and fittings which did not comply with the specification or the drawings. The architect was failing to inspect the work effectively so the client did his own inspection and informed the builder that the work was not being carried out properly.

It had been agreed at the start of the contract that valuations (assessments of work for payment), and the corresponding cheques from the clients would be weekly. The builder was overvaluing the work he had done in order to get more money out of the clients than he was entitled to. The builder objected to the clients' inspection of his work. The clients objected to the builder's overvaluations. Weekly valuations had been adhered to up to this point.

The builder repeatedly threatened to leave the job, saying that he was dissatisfied with the clients. It emerged afterwards that the builder was in financial trouble and was possibly going bankrupt, so he was deliberately overvaluing his work in order to get as much money as possible out of the clients, with the intention of closing down his business and starting up under a new name.

A cheque was presented to the builder as a consequence of another (over)valuation. The builder then disappeared, abandoning the contract, under the impression that the cheque had cleared. But at the eleventh hour the clients were able to stop the cheque, feeling their action to be justified as the builder had overcharged them and disappeared. The builder, then forced to reappear, was grossly unpleasant to the clients, and threatened them with legal action for breach of contract.

The architect, in the meantime, had been approached by the clients regarding the valuations (the architect's responsibility). The architect always gave the same answer: 'In my professional opinion the valuations represent a fair and accurate assessment of the work completed to date' (or words to that effect). In other words a statement that bore no specific relevance to the clients' particular grievance, just a stock answer which protected both architect and builder.

After an argument the builder finally left the site (minus the cheque) and the architect was sacked. The builder's workforce initially left with the builder but were dissatisfied with their employment and returned to A and K's house, offering to finish the job.

The original contract was now void as the builder had abandoned the job, but the workforce agreed to carry on according to the specification and drawings, but with an extended completion date.

The clients themselves became involved in the running of the job. The wife bought and collected materials in the car and the husband did the painting to help speed up the job and enable them to occupy more of the house.

The scaffolding which had been erected at the back of the house was dismantled and taken away as that part of the work was finished. The Environmental Health Officer then appeared and condemned the external plumbing and rainwater pipework installed by the original builder at the back of the house, and said that it had to be replaced. Scaffolding had to be re-erected, and as it was a terraced house the only access was through the newly decorated rooms. The costs involved in re-erecting the scaffolding and putting right the plumbing pipework were borne by the clients, even though they had paid for the work once already.

The scaffolding was dismantled again and brought back through the house, with the subsequent making good and repainting done by the clients. (The costs involved in scaffolding are mainly in erection and dismantling – so hardly any saving was made by only using it for a short period.)

The remaining workforce made frequent requests for money. There was now almost no control over material and wage costs, or the time spent on the site. Much of the original work had to be altered because of bad workmanship.

Some incidents were almost farcical. The basement toilet which had been used throughout the job had been taken out. Two painters were working outside on the extension roof. One of the painters, particularly partial to curry, used a toilet on an intermediate floor which, while being fully fitted and connected inside, had not been finally 'coupled up' outside. The effects of the flush were a narrow miss for the other painter working outside, a direct hit on the extension roof, and a resulting splash through an open window back into the house. On a separate occasion, after carpets and curtains had been fitted, a toilet cistern leaked and brought down a ceiling. The soggy mess cascaded down the stairs and the whole stair carpet had to be replaced. On another occasion a carpenter fitting a pelmet dropped a whole tin of paint on the hall carpet, which had been down for just two hours. On yet another occasion, with the roof not completely finished and therefore not watertight, the whole area was struck by flash floods. Rainwater poured in through the roof, and all the clients were able to do was to put plastic dustbins under the hole. The rain was so heavy that the dustbins filled every 15 minutes. Again, carpets had to be replaced and decorations made good.

The couple agreed that with hindsight a new builder and a new contract would have been a much more satisfactory solution than trying to run the job themselves on a day-to-day basis.

Retention sums, which were part of the original contract (to cover the defects liability period), were now inapplicable, as were any guarantees on workmanship, and the whole job had cost between £10,000–£12,000 more than the original estimate.

It is easy to be wise after the event but, faced with the same problems, how would the average person handle them?

It is by noting the experiences of others and judging the consequences that people become better equipped to know what action to take when confronted with similar situations themselves.

Chapter 12

Taking Legal Action

If all else fails in a serious dispute with someone whom you have employed, you are faced with the choice of forgetting what has happened and writing off any debts that have accrued, or taking some form of legal action.

Some people cannot begin to contemplate taking action in the courts, whereas others will insist on their rights as a matter of principle and will not think twice about attempting legal proceedings. Obviously, in most cases it depends on the amount involved and whether there is likely to be a counter claim. So a careful assessment of the situation should be the first thing you attend to, and if the sum of money involved is substantial, or if the other party has threatened you with legal action, the first thing you should do is take legal advice.

Try to assess also whether the person you wish to take action against has any money or assets, otherwise your successful court case could be a victory on paper only (eg if a company or an individual is insolvent). Never attempt major legal action on your own. It is too complex a subject for anyone without the proper qualifications and experience. If you were to attempt it, you would probably find that whoever you were suing had a clever legal representative whose experience gave him a distinct advantage over you.

You can get free advice from Citizens' Advice Bureaux and community law centres on the procedure for taking legal action. (Look for the addresses and telephone numbers in your telephone book.) Local authorities will also advise on court procedure and form filling but will not give legal advice.

Sometimes just writing to the other party in the dispute using a semi-legal format (ie threatening to consult a solicitor with a view to legal proceedings) will prompt a settlement.

Damages

If the client sues the contractor successfully for breach of contract there are two possible outcomes, either:

- the contractor has to rectify whatever was wrong and complete the contract; or
- a sum of money is agreed as payment to the client from the contractor. This sum of money is to cover 'damages' suffered by the client, and should be sufficient to cover the costs of employing another contractor to rectify faults caused by the first contractor, and to complete the contract.

'Damages' is a more likely outcome of successful legal action against a contractor, as the alternative would mean that he would re-start work on your property – something that would doubtless be unsatisfactory to both parties concerned. Liquidated damages (see page 104) would also be assessed in a breach of contract action.

Small claims

Small claims are dealt with by the County Courts. If the total cost of your claim is not more than £500 (England and Wales; but the amount is under review – 1989), you can take action yourself without a solicitor. The small claims procedure is simple and informal, and is set out in an excellent booklet entitled *Small Claims in the County Court* by Michael Birks, available free of charge from County Court offices or Citizens' Advice Bureaux. The court office will advise you on how to go about your claim and will provide the necessary forms. They will not give legal advice.

An outline of the procedure is as follows:

- Write to the person you have a claim against (the defendant) and state your complaints. Send the letter by recorded delivery and keep a copy.
- If there is no favourable response, send another letter to the defendant stating that you will give him 14 days to settle your claim, otherwise you will start legal proceedings. Send it by recorded delivery and keep a copy.
- If there is no response, go to the court office (it has to be the local

County Court in the area where the defendant lives or has his business), and take with you a statement of the facts of the case and a list of the amounts you are claiming. You can add interest (currently 15 per cent per annum) to the total.

- The court office will give you a 'form for requesting issue of a summons' which you (as plaintiff) fill in with the statement of facts and the amount you are claiming. You have to pay a fee for the issue of a summons and this cost can be added to your claim. Fees are currently 10 per cent up to £300 and £37 for claims between £300 and £500.
- The court then issues a summons to the defendant with a form for him to state his defence, and his counterclaim if he has one, of which you get a copy. Any defended claim under £500 is automatically dealt with by arbitration.
- A date is then set for a preliminary hearing which is attended by plaintiff and defendant. Depending upon the outcome of this hearing a full hearing is scheduled where witnesses can be called.
- The full hearing is normally conducted in a room in the courthouse, not in an open court, and the registrar listens to both sides and to any witnesses. He then delivers his judgment, which is final and cannot normally be appealed against.

Larger claims

Claims up to £5000 are dealt with at the County Court (not using the small claims procedure), with appeals to the High Court. Claims over £5000 are heard at the High Court, with appeals to the Court of Appeal.

You would be advised to have legal representation when taking action in the higher courts as the procedure is complicated and requires expert handling for the best results.

Scotland

The corresponding small claims procedure is dealt with by the Sheriff Court, which allows you to handle your own case up to a maximum claim of £750, and is part of the *summary cause procedure*, which is used for claims not exceeding £1500. Two booklets, *A Guide to Small Claims in the Sheriff Court* and *A Guide to Summary Cause Procedure in the Sheriff Court*, are available free from the Sheriff Clerk's office.

Appendices

National telephone dialling codes are given, although local codes may differ. Please note that the London telephone area code changed on 6 May 1990 and 01 became either 071 (central area) or 081. The new codes are given here.

Supply of Goods and Services Act 1982

This Act is in two parts, the first covering goods and the second services. It covers the law on consumers' rights and traders' obligations in England, Wales and Northern Ireland, but not in Scotland.

Goods
This part of the act relates to goods supplied:

- as part of a service – for example, light fittings installed by an electrician;
- in part exchange – for example, a new appliance where the old one has been traded in;
- on hire – for example, power tools for DIY jobs, ladders and trestles.

The Act states that such goods must be:

- of merchantable quality – for example, light fittings must work and be safe;
- as described – for example, if window frames are plastic the dealer must not say they are made of wood;
- fit for any particular purpose made known to the supplier – for example, a ladder must be long enough to reach the height you told the shop you wanted it to reach.

If goods fail to meet these requirements you are entitled to claim a full or partial refund.

Services
This part of the Act relates to the quality of services provided by contractors working in your home, and also covers those away from the home such as appliance repairers. It is particularly relevant to people who employ builders and other contractors, and states what you ought to be able to expect from a service for which you are charged.

A firm or an individual providing a service must do so:

- within a reasonable time – for example, installing a new pump for your central heating system should not take two months;
- for a reasonable charge – for example, £400 to replace two small panes of glass would be grossly excessive;

(These two rights exist where nothing is said in the contract about time or charge.)

- with reasonable care and skill – for example, building work must be carried out by a suitably qualified person to a proper standard of workmanship. (This right exists even if nothing is written or stated at the outset of dealings with your contractor, or your written contract does not mention it.)

What is 'reasonable'?

The definition of 'reasonable' in this context is decided by what is considered normal and appropriate for the type of job being undertaken. If a professional is handling your contract he will know from experience what is and is not reasonable. If you have to judge for yourself, comparison with similar work, perhaps at the homes of friends and neighbours, is the simplest way to find out. Failing that you will have to have an expert opinion.

If suppliers and contractors do not stick to these rules you have cause for complaint, and may be entitled to compensation. As with all disputes and complaints, though, always try to get a satisfactory solution to your problem amicably rather than by using a legal process.

Scotland

As already stated, the above Act does not apply but the law has three similar rules covering 'merchantable quality', 'as described', and 'fit for a particular purpose'. Some firms belong to trade associations and some trade associations will help with disputes. Codes of practice exist which give guidelines for looking after customers, and low-cost arbitration schemes operate to help settle disputes. Contractors must use 'reasonable care' when working for you. If you have a complaint and negotiation/arbitration has not worked, you will have to resort to the courts (page 121).

Professional and Trade Associations

These organisations exist primarily to represent and protect their members but 'codes of practice' and safety/workmanship standards are there to benefit customers as well.

Using a professional or a contractor who is associated with one of them will offer some protection and assistance in the event of problems with your contract.

A brief description of their activities is included under each heading, along with details of codes of practice and guarantee/warranty schemes.

Please note that the London telephone area code changed on 6 May 1990, and 01 became either 071 (central area) or 081. The new codes are given here.

Professional organisations (see also Chapter 4)

Architects
The professional body representing architects is the Royal Institute of British Architects (RIBA), 66 Portland Place, London W1N 4AD; 071-580 5533. It operates a code of professional conduct by which its members are governed. A copy of the code can be obtained from the RIBA, which can look into complaints relating to the code. These include:

- improper conduct concerning a client's affairs
- dishonesty
- lack of integrity
- conflict of interests.

In Scotland, the Royal Incorporation of Architects in Scotland (RIAS), 15 Rutland Square, Edinburgh EH1 2BE; 031-229 7205, has a similar code.

A dispute or difference can, by agreement between both parties, be referred to the relevant professional body for an opinion, provided that:

- the member's appointment is based on the document provided by the

professional body and has been confirmed in writing;
- the opinion is sought on a joint statement of undisputed facts;
- the parties undertake to accept the opinion as final and binding upon them.

Any dispute or difference which cannot be resolved by the above can be referred to the Chartered Institute of Arbitrators (see below), if both parties agree – (in Scotland to the Dean of the Faculty of Advocates). Disputes over fees can also be looked into by the RIBA.

The Royal Society of Ulster Architects (RSUA)
2 Mount Charles
Belfast BT7 1NZ
0232 323760

The Society of Architects in Wales
75A Llandennis Road
Rhydypennau
Cardiff CF2 6EE
0222 762215

Surveyors
The professional body representing chartered surveyors is the Royal Institution of Chartered Surveyors (RICS), 12 Great George Street, Parliament Square, London SW1P 3AD; 071-222 7000. The RICS, like the RIBA, operates a code of conduct, a copy of which can be obtained from the address above. The Professional Practice Department will look into disputes involving:

- dishonesty
- professional misconduct.

For other disputes there is an arbitration scheme administered by the Chartered Institute of Arbitrators, International Arbitration Centre, 75 Cannon Street, London EC4N 5BH; 071-236 8761. This is an independent body which also administers other arbitration schemes for consumer and insurance disputes. You can only use the arbitration scheme if both parties agree. There is a fee (£57.50, including VAT – 1989 rate) for registration which either party may be able to claim back if successful.

If you lose, you cannot subsequently sue your surveyor in the courts over the same issue. If you win, the arbitrator may decide to refund your fee, and any compensation award becomes due within a specified time and is legally enforceable in the courts.

Structural engineers

The professional body representing structural engineers is the Institution of Structural Engineers (ISE), 11 Upper Belgrave Street, London SW1X 8BH; 071-235 4535. It also operates a code of conduct, with rules relating to responsibility, dignity and reputation of the profession, and integrity. The professional practice committee will look into allegations of misconduct against its members and may take some disciplinary action, but they will not act as mediators in disputes between members and clients. However, in the event of a complaint they may agree to an independent arbitration.

Trade organisations

Builders

Employing builders can be a risky business, so in order to give yourself some protection and guarantee you could use one who is a member of either the Building Employers Confederation or the Federation of Master Builders.

Building Employers Confederation (BEC)
82 New Cavendish Street
London W1M 8AD
071-580 5588

Members of the BEC can offer a guarantee scheme for building works whether a professional is used or not. You can contact the BEC Building Trust Ltd, 18 Mansfield Street, London W1M 9FG; 071-580 6306, for a list of its members who operate the guarantee scheme in your area. Contracts worth between £500 and £40,000 (excluding VAT) are eligible for the scheme if you employ the builder directly, and if a professional acts for you the upper limit is £50,000 (excluding VAT). The cost of the scheme is 1 per cent of the total contract price, and benefits include:

- a formal written contract;
- a guarantee that the contract will be adhered to;
- if a member defaults or goes bankrupt, the Trust will ensure that another member finishes the job, and additional costs up to £6500 will be met by the scheme;
- the availability of an independent conciliator to help resolve any problems that arise, and an arbitration service if necessary – on contracts where a professional is not used (using a professional with a JCT contract provides for arbitration);
- any faults that occur within a six-month period will be corrected;
- full insurance cover for damage during the contract;

131

- structural faults occurring within two years and related to the work carried out will be rectified.

The scheme must be negotiated before work starts and full details can be obtained from the BEC. The scheme operates in England and Wales, but not in Scotland by the Scottish Building Employers Federation, 13 Woodside Crescent, Glasgow G3 7UP; 041-332 7144.

Federation of Master Builders (FMB)
Gordon Fisher House
33 John Street
London WC1N 2BB
071-242 7583

The Federation operates the National Register of Warranted Builders. Contact the FMB for assistance in finding a builder who will operate the scheme. Contracts up to £75,000 (including VAT) can be included in the scheme whether you use a professional or not, provided they are negotiated before the work is started.

The cost of the scheme is 1 per cent of the total contract price, and benefits include:

- proven additional costs, incurred through having to find another builder should the first builder fail to complete, of up to £10,000;
- completion work to be undertaken by another registered builder of the client's choice;
- any defects through faulty materials or workmanship reported within two years after completion of the work will be rectified (if agreed) at no expense to the client;
- that the builder holds current insurance policies for damage;
- free conciliation/arbitration service for disputes between builder and client.

For full details of the scheme, contact the FMB.

Electricians

Safety is the overriding factor when any electrical work is undertaken. Never attempt installations or repairs yourself unless you know exactly what you are doing.

If you need an electrician it is in your own interests to use one who is competent, such as those approved by the National Inspection Council for Electrical Installation Contracting (NICEIC), Vintage House, 36 Albert Embankment, London SE1 7UJ; 071-735 1322, or the Electrical Contractors' Association (ECA), Central Court, Knoll Rise, Orpington, Kent BR6 0JA; 0689 70538.

NICEIC is a consumer safety organisation whose members' work must conform to the regulations of the Institution of Electrical Engineers (IEE), Savoy Place, London WC2R 0BL; 071-240 1871, and to British Standards codes of practice.

The ECA is the contractors' trade association and it operates a completion guarantee scheme which allows for:

- the additional cost of completion of work should the original contractor become insolvent.

There is also a guarantee of work scheme which guarantees:

- to put right any work by a member which does not comply with the relevant standards.

The Electrical Contractors' Association of Scotland, 23 Heriot Row, Edinburgh EH3 6EW; 031-225 7221, also has a code of good practice and a procedure for handling complaints by clients.

Details of schemes and names of contractors can be obtained by writing to the addresses shown.

Glazing contractors

A code of practice has been drawn up and agreed between the Glass and Glazing Federation (GGF), 44–48 Borough High Street, London SE1 1XB; 071-403 7177, and the Office of Fair Trading (OFT), Field House, 15–25 Breams Buildings, London EC4A 1PR; 071-242 2858. It covers advertising, selling, quality, complaints etc and keeping to the code is a condition of membership. To benefit from the code you should make sure that you use a GGF member. Benefits include:

- protection of deposits paid to GGF members through the Deposit Indemnity Fund of up to £2500;
- arrangements for completion of a job by another GGF member;
- insurance to cover any damage;
- materials that conform to British Standards;
- availability of a low-cost arbitration scheme set up by the GGF and administered by the Chartered Institute of Arbitrators.

Before having double glazing installed you should check with your local authority that the units comply with the building regulations in respect of ventilation, means of escape in case of fire etc. You may also need permission to use certain styles and types of materials, especially in a conservation area or if the building is listed. Again check with your local authority.

Contact the GGF for a list of members in your area. A range of leaflets is also available.

Heating installers

Fuel, water and electricity are all needed when a central heating system is installed, so it is important to make sure that the installer is competent and experienced. Fuels can be gas, oil or solid fuel. There is a legal requirement to comply with the Gas Safety Regulations and installers can be fined for failing to observe them.

The Confederation for the Registration of Gas Installers (CORGI), St Martin's House, 140 Tottenham Court Road, London W1P 9LN; 071-387 9185, is an organisation set up at government instigation by the gas industry and trade associations in the heating, plumbing and building industries. Its function is primarily to promote gas safety, and it keeps a register of competent installers who work to Gas Safety Regulations and British Standards codes of practice.

The CORGI register for your area can be inspected at your local gas showroom or consumer advice centre.

CORGI (Scottish Region)
Granton House, West Granton Road, Edinburgh EH 5 1YB;
031-552 6960

CORGI (Wales Region)
Snelling House, Bute Terrace, Cardiff CF1 2UF; 0222 395398

The Heating and Ventilating Contractors' Association (HVCA), ESCA House, 34 Palace Court, London W2 4JG; 071-229 2488, represents central heating contractors and offers a double guarantee scheme to customers. The guarantee is for 12 months and covers:

* workmanship
* materials
* performance.

You are also protected:

* if the installer does not honour the guarantee. The HVCA will meet the cost of putting things right;
* if the installer becomes insolvent or bankrupt. The HVCA will honour the guarantee and finish an incomplete installation.

Leaflets and details are available from HVCA.

HVCA (Scotland)
Bush House, Bush Estate, Penicuik, Midlothian EH26 0SB; 031-445 5580

HVCA (Northern Ireland)
c/o A Crawford, Crawford & Co, 16 Donegal Square South,
Belfast BT1 5PA; 0232 321731

The National Association of Plumbing, Heating and Mechanical Services Contractors (NAPH & MSC), 6 Gate Street, London WC2A 3HX; 071-405 2678, and the Scottish and Northern Ireland Plumbing Employers' Federation, 2 Walker Street, Edinburgh EH3 7LB; 031-225 2255, are trade associations. The NAPH & MSC operates a warranty scheme to cover new and existing central heating systems. Information about the scheme is available from NAPH & MSC member firms.

Insulation contractors
The National Cavity Insulation Association (NCIA), PO Box 12, Haslemere, Surrey GU27 3AN; 0428 54011, has a list of installing members for cavity wall insulation. It operates a code of professional practice which includes the following:

- fair and honest dealing towards customers;
- compliance with statutory regulations governing cavity wall insulation, and technical standards for product and workmanship;
- availability of arbitration in the event of a complaint.

Members of the National Association of Loft Insulation Contractors, PO Box 12, Haslemere, Surrey GU27 3AN; 0428 54011, operate to a code of professional practice and will investigate complaints by customers relating to workmanship and materials.

The organisation representing draught proofing contractors is the Draught Proofing Advisory Association, PO Box 12, Haslemere, Surrey GU27 3AN; 0428 54011, and that concerned with cavity foam insulation is the Cavity Foam Bureau, PO Box 79, Oldbury, Warley, West Midlands B69 4PW; 021-544 4949. Both organisations offer an investigation of complaints procedure. Further information about any of the above associations can be obtained by writing to them.

Plumbers
This is one of the most unprotected of industries, especially in the domestic field. There is almost no control over standards of workmanship, and customers are often at the mercy of whoever they can get.

The Institute of Plumbing, however, maintains a register of plumbers and will look into complaints by customers against a 'registered plumber'. As a last resort it can strike off the list any plumber who acts incompetently. The Institute of Plumbing can be contacted at 64 Station Lane, Hornchurch, Essex RM12 6NB; 04024 72791.

Unvented pressurised hot water systems are now permitted in this country (1989). They are hot water cylinders (like the one you have in your airing cupboard) that work directly off the incoming water main, without the need for a cold water storage tank. If you want one installed, make sure that your installer is approved under the certification scheme operated by the British Board of Agrément, as a wrongly installed system can be dangerous.

Other organisations, already mentioned under 'Heating installers', are the National Association of Plumbing, Heating and Mechanical Services Contractors (NAPH & MSC), and the Scottish and Northern Ireland Plumbing Employers' Federation. Again, information can be obtained by writing to the organisations concerned.

Roofing contractors

Roofing is another industry lacking in proper control of workmanship and materials standards. The difficulties for the customer are that inspection of roofing work is often not possible, and that finished jobs cannot always be 'tested' before payment is made.

The trade organisation for roofing companies is the National Federation of Roofing Contractors (NFRC) which, among other things, expects its members to comply with British Standards materials specifications, and to work to agreed codes of practice.

A guarantee scheme is available and details can be obtained by writing to the NFRC. Its address is: 24 Weymouth Street, London W1N 3FA; 071-436 0387.

This list is not exhaustive, and further information about various organisations, associations and federations can be obtained from:

- Citizens' Advice Bureaux
- consumer advice centres
- The Office of Fair Trading
- local authorities
- public libraries.

It is worth contacting these organisations to see what they have to offer in the way of customer service and protection, whether you avail yourself of it or not. At least you will know what is available and can make a decision with all the relevant information to hand.

Appendix 3
Useful Addresses

General

Architects Registration Council of the United Kingdom
73 Hallam Street, London W1N 6EE; 071-580 5861
Association of British Insurers
Aldermary House, Queen Street, London EC4N 1TT; 071-248 4477
Association of Consultant Architects
7 Park Street, Bristol BS1 5NF; 0272 293379
British Board of Agrément
PO Box 195, Bucknalls Lane, Garston, Watford, Hertfordshire
WD2 7NG; 0923 670844
British Chemical Damp Course Association
16A Whitchurch Road, Pangbourne, Berkshire RG8 7BP; 0734
843799
British Gas
Rivermill House, 152 Grosvenor Road, London SW1V 3JN; 071-
821 1444
British Safety Council
62 Chancellors Road, London W6 9RS; 081-741 1231
British Standards Institution
2 Park Street, London W1A 2BS; 071-629 9000
Building Centres
26 Store Street, London WC1E 7BT; 071-637 3151
general enquiries 0344 884999
115 Portland Street, Manchester M1 6FB 061-236 9802
131 West Nile Street, Glasgow G1 2RX 041-333 9701
and other major towns and cities
Building Research Establishment
Bucknalls Lane, Garston, Watford, Hertfordshire WD2 7JR; 0923
894040
Central Electricity Generating Board
Sudbury House, 15 Newgate Street, London EC1A 7AU; 071-634
5111

Chartered Institute of Building
  Englemere, King's Ride, Ascot, Berkshire SL5 8BJ; 0990 23355
Consumers' Association
  2 Marylebone Road, London NW1 4DX; 071-486 5544
Customs and Excise (VAT)
  Headquarters: King's Beam House, Mark Lane, London EC3R
  7HE; 071-626 1515 and local offices
Department of the Environment
  Headquarters: 2 Marsham Street, London SW1P 3EB; 071-276 3000
  for general enquiries 071-276 0990 or local offices
Electricity Consumers' Council
  Brook House, Torrington Place, London WC1E 7LL; 071-636 5703;
  not for individual complaints.
Gas Consumer Council
  Head office: Abford House, 15 Wilton Road, London SW1V 1LT;
  071-931 0977
Health and Safety Commission
  Regina House, 259 Old Marylebone Road, London NW1 5RR;
  071-229 3456
Historic Buildings and Monuments Commission for England
  Fortress House, 23 Savile Row, London W1X 1AB; 071-734 6010
Historic Buildings Scotland
  Scottish Development Office, 20 Brandon Street, Edinburgh EH3
  5DX; 031-226 2570
Historic Buildings Wales
  CADW Brunel House, 2 Fitzalan Road, Cardiff CF2 1UY; 0222
  465511
Institute of Building Control
  21 High Street, Ewell, Epsom, Surrey KT17 1SB; 081-393 6860
Law Society
  113 Chancery Lane, London WC2A 1PL; 071-242 1222
Law Society for Scotland
  26 Drumsheugh Gardens, Edinburgh EH3 7YR; 031-226 7411
National Home Improvement Council
  19 Store Street, London WC1E 7BT; 071-636 2562
Planning Aid for Londoners
  100 Minories, London EC3N 1JY; 071-702 0051
RIBA Publications Ltd
  Finsbury Mission, 39 Moreland Street, London EC1V 8BB;
  071-251 0791
Royal Town Planning Institute
  26 Portland Place, London W1N 4BE; 071-636 9107
  15 Rutland Square, Edinburgh EH1 2BE; 031-337 3423
Society for the Protection of Ancient Buildings
  37 Spital Square, London E1 6DY; 071-377 1644

Solid Fuel Advisory Service
  Hobart House, Grosvenor Place, London SW1X 7AW; 071-235
  2020

Firms providing damp proofing and timber treatment service

Dampcoursing Ltd
  10 Dorset Road, London N15 5AJ; 081-802 2233
Peter Cox Group Ltd
  Heritage House, 234 High Street, Sutton, Surrey SM1 1MX; 081-642 9444
Rentokil Ltd
  43A Selsdon Road, Croydon, Surrey CR2 6PY; 081-686 9291

Manufacturers of products in general use

Aga – cooking and heating equipment
  PO Box 30, Ketley, Telford TF1 3BR; 0952 641100
Alpine Co Ltd – double glazing
  Alpine House, Honeypot Lane, London NW9 9RU; 081-204 3393
  dial 100 and ask for Freefone Alpine
Armitage Shanks – bathroom equipment
  303 High Holborn, London WC1V 3JZ; 071-405 9663
Barlo Products – heating equipment
  Barlo House, Finway, Dallow Road, Luton, Bedfordshire LU1
  1TR; 0582 480333
Carradon Twyfords Ltd – bathroom equipment
  PO Box 23, Shelton New Road, Cliffe Vale, Stoke on Trent ST4
  7AL; 0270 879777
Celcon Ltd – aerated concrete building blocks
  Celcon House, 289 High Holborn, London WC1V 7HU; 071-242
  9766
Crabtree Electrical Industries Ltd – electrical equipment
  Lincoln Works, Walsall, West Midlands WS1 2DN; 0922 721202
Delmar nmc Ltd – decorative mouldings
  Manor Royal, Crawley, West Sussex RH10 2XQ; 0293 546251
Dulux Trade Group, ICI paints – paint and woodcare products
  Wexham Road, Slough, Berkshire SL2 5DS; 0753 31151
Everest – double glazing
  Everest House, Sopers Road, Potters Bar, Hertfordshire EN6 4SG;
  0707 875700
Franke (UK) Ltd – sinks
  Suite 15b, International Office Centre, Styal Road, Manchester M22
  5WB; 061-436 6280

Glow-worm TI Ltd – central heating boilers
  Nottingham Road, Belper, Derbyshire DE5 1JT; 077 382 4141
Hodkin & Jones (Sheffield) Ltd – decorative room mouldings
  Callywhite Lane, Dronfield, Sheffield S18 6XP; 0246 290890
Ideal Standard Ltd – bathroom equipment
  PO Box 60, Kingston upon Hull HU5 4JE; 0482 46461
Kango Wolf Power Tools Ltd
  PO Box 379, Hanger Lane, London W5 1DS; 081-998 2911
MFI Furniture Centres – budget kitchens and furniture
  Head office: 333 The Hyde, London NW9 6TD; 081-200 8000
Mira (Walker Crosweller & Co Ltd) – shower equipment
  Whaddon Works, Cheltenham, Gloucestershire GL52 1BR; 0242
  527 953
MK Electric Ltd – electrical equipment
  Shrubbery Road, London N9 0PA; 081-807 5151
Myson Heating – radiators
  Eastern Avenue, Team Valley Trading Estate, Gateshead, Tyne and
  Wear NE11 0PG; 091-482 5418
PC Henderson Ltd – garage doors and sliding doors
  Ashton Road, Harold Hill, Romford, Essex RM3 8UL; 04023 45555
Potterton International – central heating equipment
  Portobello Works, Emscote Road, Warwick CV34 5QU; 0926
  493471
Runtalrad – stylish made-to-order radiators
  Ridgeway Industrial Estate, Ridgeway Road, Iver, Buckinghamshire
  SL0 9JQ; 0753 655215
Sphinx Tiles – range of floor and wall tiles
  Bath Road, Thatcham, Newbury, Berkshire RG13 4NQ; 0635 65475
Stelrad Group Ltd – central heating equipment
  Accord House, Goulton Street, Kingston upon Hull HU3 4DJ;
  0482 223 673
Velux Co Ltd – roof lights (windows)
  Gunnelswood Road, Stevenage, Hertfordshire; 0438 312570
Volex Electrical Products Ltd – electrical equipment and accessories
  Leigh Road, Hindley Green, Wigan, Lancashire WN2 4XY; 0942
  57100

Large builders' merchants and do-it-yourself stores

These can be useful for seeing what products are available in
connection with work that you intend having done. Some have
displays of kitchen and bathroom equipment.

CP Hart & Sons – builders' and plumbers' merchants
Arch 213, Newham Terrace, Hercules Road, London SE1 7LD;
071-928 5866

Jewsons Ltd – timber and builders' merchants
Warwick Place, High Street, Uxbridge, Middlesex UB8 1HL; 0895
38200; and branches

Magnet Ltd – windows, doors, joinery and accessories
Head office: Royd Ings Avenue, Keighley, West Yorkshire BD21
4BY; 0535 661133; and branches

Travis Perkins plc – timber and builders' merchants
Group head office: 149 Harrow Road, Paddington, London W2
6NA; 071-412 0081; and branches

B & Q – DIY stores
Head office: Portswood House, 1 Hampshire Corporate Park,
Chandlers Ford, Eastleigh, Hampshire SO5 3YX; 0703 256256; and
branches

Payless DIY Ltd
80 Bushey Road, London SW20; 081-879 7400; and branches

Sainsbury's Homebase – DIY stores
Warwick Road, London W14 8PU; 071-603 6397; and branches

Texas Homecare – DIY stores
Head office: Home Charm House, Park Farm, Wellingborough,
Northamptonshire NN8 3XA; 0933 679679; and branches

WHS Do-it-all Ltd – DIY stores
Head office: Falcon House, The Minories, Dudley, West Midlands
DY2 8PG; 0384 456456; and branches

Wickes DIY Superstores
Head office: Wickes House, 120–138 Station Road, Harrow,
Middlesex HA1 2QB; 081-863 5696; and branches

Further Reading

Grants

Home Improvement Grants: a guide for home owners, landlords and tenants, Department of the Environment, housing booklet no 14 (HMSO)

The building regulations

The Building Regulations (HMSO)
The Building Regulations Explained and Illustrated (7th edition), Vincent Powell-Smith and MJ Billington (Collins Professional)
Guide to the Building Regulations 1985, AJ Elder (Architectural Press)

General information

Alteration or Conversion of Houses, JF Garner and R Edmunds (Longman)
Bazaar Property Doctor, Ian Morris (BBC Books)
Buying and Renovating Houses for Profit, 2nd edn, K Ludman and RD Buchanan (Kogan Page)
Care for Old Houses, Pamela Cunnington (Prism Alpha)
Common Building Defects – Diagnosis and Remedy, (Longman Scientific and Technical)
A Concise Building Encyclopaedia, ed T Corkhill (Pitman)
House and Cottage Conversion – Guide to the Do's and Don'ts, Hugh Lander (Acanthus Books)
How to Buy and Renovate a Cottage, Stuart Turner (Kogan Page)
How to Restore and Improve your Victorian House, Alan Johnson (David and Charles)
Making the Most of Professional Services (Which? Books)
Party Walls and What to Do with them, John Anstey (Surveyors Publications)
The Penguin Dictionary of Building, John Scott (Penguin Books)
Readers Digest DIY Manual (Readers Digest)

The Small Building Contractor and the Client, Derek Miles (Intermediate Technology Publications)
Understanding JCT Building Contracts, David Chappell (International Thomson Business Publishing)

Layout and decor

Terence Conran's New House Book (Conran Octopus Ltd)

Legal
The Homeowner's Guide to the Law, Cedric Meadowcroft (Fourmat Publishing)

Common Technical Terms and Jargon

Contractors and professionals often use words which mean very little to the average person. This can cause a lot of confusion, so to help you understand what is being talked about some of those regularly used are listed here.

Agent. A representative of the contractor who supervises the work.
Architrave. Decorative wooden moulding around a door or window, to cover the joint between the wall and the frame.

Bonding. Type of thick plaster used as an initial coat to cover brickwork.

Chainsaw. Electric or petrol-driven saw used for trees or heavy timber.
Chippies. Carpenters.
Circular saw. Electric saw used for fast cutting of timber.
Combi. Combination boiler. Provides both central heating and hot water for washing from the same unit.
Consumer unit. Box containing main electrical switch and fuses or circuit breakers.
Crimping. Method of joining electrical cables.

DS. District Surveyor.
Dubbing-out. Filling out an uneven surface with plaster or sand/cement to provide a flat finish for a final coat.
Duct. An enclosure or channel for running pipework and cables (or see *Extract* below).

Extract. Fan or duct for removing stale air or fumes.

Felt and batten. Laying roofing felt and strips of timber on to rafters prior to fixing tiles or slates.
FFL. Finished floor level. Often used on drawings to enable contractors to mark positions before the floor is laid.
Flashing. Sheet lead, zinc or copper fitted to prevent water from penetrating the joints where a vertical surface, eg a wall or chimney stack, projects through the roof.

144

Head. Terminating point for incoming main electricity cable.

Joist. Horizontal timbers which carry floors and ceilings.

Kango. Electric or compressed air hammer used for breaking concrete or making large holes in walls.

Lintel. A horizontal beam across an opening (usually a door or window) to carry the weight above.

Main. Gas, electricity or water incoming supply.
MDF. Medium density fibre board, used for kitchen worktops, cupboards etc.
Mixer. An electric or petrol-driven machine for mixing sand and cement on site. Also, a device for blending hot and cold water in a shower.

Newell post. Vertical post on a staircase to which the banister rail is attached.
Noggin. A short piece of timber used as a brace to strengthen parallel lengths of timber.

PAR. Planed all round. Timber that has been planed, as opposed to sawn (see *Sawn timber*).
Ply. Plywood. Sheets of timber bonded together to various thicknesses.

QS. Quantity Surveyor.

Rafter. An inclined beam supporting a roof.
Ready mix. Pre-mixed concrete or sand/cement delivered to site in wet form by lorries.
Render. A coat of sand/cement or plaster applied to a wall.
Repointing. Scraping out loose sand/cement between bricks and re-filling with fresh sand/cement.
Riser. The vertical part of a stair that joins the tread at a right angle.
Rising main. Water main that rises up a building serving points on the way.
RSJ. Rolled steel joist, usually used to support the weight bearing down where a wall has been removed.

Sash weights. Lead or cast iron weights used in sliding sash windows to balance the weight of the window itself.
Sawn timber. Timber that has been cut into lengths, but has not been planed.
Scratch coat. Coat of plaster or sand/cement which has been 'scratched' to form a key for the next coat.

Screed. A layer (usually of sand/cement mix) applied over a concrete floor slab and trowelled smooth. Pipes and cables are sometimes buried in it.

Skim. A thin layer (a few millimetres) of plaster as a finishing coat.

Skip. A large rubbish container, delivered and collected by special trucks.

Skirting. A protective strip fitted between wall and floor. It can be timber, sand/cement or plaster.

Snagging. Correcting defects at the end of a job prior to finishing.

Soaker. A piece of lead or zinc formed into a right angle and bonded with slates or tiles to make a watertight joint between a wall and a roof.

Soffit. Boarding fitted under parts of a building, eg under the eaves.

Sparks. Electricians.

Spec. Specification.

Spread. A plasterer.

Subbies. Sub-contractors.

Tails. Heavy duty wires used to connect an electricity meter.

T and G. Tongued and grooved. Boarding that has a groove in one edge and a tongue on the other. The boards lock together.

Tower. Portable scaffold which slots together.

Tread. The part of a stair that you tread on.

Index